The book that **DARES YOU**

to pick it up and **not to laugh**;

otherwise, **double your money back***

---

* To be paid by author to Jews only. Reader stands in a Barnes & Noble or
Borders store in St. Louis while author reads chapters in front of a crowd
and reader does not chuckle. Exclusions: Anyone who cannot hear or
is out of his or her mind. Proof of purchase and Jewishness necessary:
Must show proof of circumcision or bris-kit by certified mohel.

CHARITABLE CONTRIBUTIONS

*A portion of the proceeds from the
sale of this book will be donated to:*

THE OBSESSIVE COMPULSIVE FOUNDATION
in New Haven, Connecticut

ST. LOUIS OBSESSIVE COMPULSIVE
DISORDER (OCD) SUPPORT GROUP

OBSESSIVE COMPULSIVE DISORDER (OCA)

JEWISH FEDERATION

SHAARE EMETH TEMPLE

THE LITTLE SYNAGOGUE,
22nd Street, New York, NY

*The people of Israel, the State of Israel,
whom I pray will soon know peace.*

Memoirs of a Born Shlepper

Never Give OCD a Third Thought

Rod Fadem

The story of a naïve, bumbling soul (a shlepper), who with the help of his guardian angel, Shlepperiel, and his innate Jewish sense of humor, overcomes his Obsessive Compulsive Disorder (OCD). He learns that his disorder has more to do with his shleppy ways than he ever dreamed.

SHLEPPEDICKE PRESS

MEMOIRS OF A BORN SHLEPPER
NEVER GIVE OCD A THIRD THOUGHT:

Copyright © 2003 by Rod Fadem

SHLEPPEDICKE PRESS
48 Highgate
St. Louis, MO 63132

Cover Design: Chuck Hathaway / Mendocino Graphics

Library of Congress Cataloging-in-Publication Data

Fadem, Rod.
    Memoirs of a born shlepper : never give OCD a third thought
/ by Rod Fadem. — 1st ed. — St. Louis, Mo. : Shleppedicke Press,
2003.
    p. ; cm.
    ISBN: 0-9742900-5-X
    1. Obsessive-compulsive disorder—Humor. 2. Obsessive-
compulsive disorder—Psychological aspects. 3. Mental health. 4.
Mental healing. I. Title.
    RC533 .F33 2003
    616.85/227—dc22   0307

Library of Congress Control Number: 2003109531

PRINTED IN THE USA
2   4   6   8   9   7   5   3   1

Acknowledgments

I wish to thank my four psychiatrists for helping me cope with obsessive compulsive disorder. Unfortunately, I'm afraid that I drove three of them to nervous breakdowns from listening to one too many of my stories and misadventures. In hindsight, I see that I should have been giving them my Xanax while they were prescribing me Prozac!

Seriously, all the events in this memoir truly happened (well, some may be tinged with one of my coping mechanisms — fantasy). I dedicate this book to all my fellow obsessive compulsive disorder sufferers, who share a common struggle, and also my psychiatrists, who truly have helped me.

There is hope.

— *The Shlepper*

A Warm Thank You Note

I wish to thank the following people
in the preparation of this memoir:

◌ My brother, Aaron, for the memory of my childhood without which I could not have reconstructed it.

◌ Rabbi Harold F. Swiss of the Little Synagogue in New York, New York, who expanded my knowledge of the Bible with his sage advice.

◌ Dr. Paul L. Schrieber, Doctor of Exegetical Theology at Concordia Seminary in St. Louis, who helped me find the joy and beauty in the Torah.

◌ Vivian Vican, the best typist in Brooklyn, who helped me greatly improve my manuscript.

◌ The St. Louis Writer's Group, who every Wednesday at Border's bookstore, patiently listened to my thirty-three rewrites and never failed to laugh.

◌ All the members of the St. Louis OCD Support Group, OCA, and Patti Perkins-Doyle of the OCFoundation, who inspired me to keep going.

◌ And thanks to my wife, Susan, for all the corrections in grammar, misspellings, and style, and for her love and support in all my endeavors.

Glossary For Goyim*

(And Some Jews)

⟡

Shlepper's Ladder

Shlepper – One who drags himself slowly through life in a drippy, messy, awkward manner.

Shmendrik – A timid, meek born loser, who is a shlemiel in training.

Shlemiel – A foolish, unlucky person; who by sheer luck can come out on top.

Mensh – A human being of the highest and noblest character

⟡

Bris – The Jewish ceremony of circumcision.

Challa – The fabulous, moist, tasty braided bread my grandmother baked.

Farshtunkener – Stinking.

***Goy** (*goyim:* plural) – Gentile. Originally meant "other people and nations."

Kop – Head of the house. Yiddishe kop as the Jewish head.

Mitzvah – One of 613 commandments. A good deed.
Plural: *Mitzvot*

Mohel – Jewish circumciser. A salami slicer who makes a great *bris*-kit.

Nudnik – Someone who is very irritating.

Nebbish – A hapless, weak sad sack.

Oy, vey – Oh, woe is me.

Shalom – Peace.

Schmaltz – Cooking fat. Melted or rendered fat, usually chicken fat.

Shikseh – A gentile girl, usually a blonde, who every Jewish boy longs for and every Jewish mother hates.

Shmeckel – A *putz*, schlong, shmuck, or penis.

Shnore – Beg or mooch.

Tepelleh – A small portable wooden potty.

Toches – Otherwise known as tochass or rear end.

Yid – A Jew.

Yiddishe – Jewish.

Zaftig – Juicy, plump, buxom. Description of a person who loves to eat schmaltz.

Memoirs of a Born Shlepper

Never Give OCD a Third Thought

Ill-yid

and the

Oy-dyssey

∾

Genesis

Trapped in a
Fallopian Tube

In the beginning was the Big Bang, a galactic orgasm that caused my mother to moan, "*Oy-y, vey-y-y.*" My startled father could only say, "Honey, honey, I can't believe it. You haven't let out a peep in years."

I still can't believe they ever had sex. I lived in the bedroom next to theirs for thirty-three years and all I heard was snoring. Perhaps my conception was an example of the trickle-down theory, such a climactic event that my mother's egg, traveling merrily along for three days, became trapped in her Fallopian tube. My father's sperm got lost. You know how male sperm hate to ask for directions. Mama's egg struggled to dislodge itself, and due to global warming her egg went from hard boiled to soft boiled to poached, and finally scrambled down to meet Mr. Right Sperm. Thousands of spermatozoa vied for the future me. This was the last time I can remember being popular.

The problem was my egg never fully coalesced. Could I ever be a real person? Eventually, my two halves united, more or less. The result was less than perfect. I lacked direction, didn't know where I was going, or what my calling would be. I would have to spend the rest of my life forming a more perfect union.

Most of my problems started in the womb. I was terrified during this Before Delivery (B.D.) period. My little brain kept repeating phrases. *Now it's five minutes B.D. Now it's three minutes B.D.* In the surrounding darkness I fell into depression and had womb anxiety, a fear of the unknown. I wondered if this early apprehension would play a dominant role in my growing up.

I loved my cozy, warm womb, but I had a burning sensation in my little heart. I had no idea what it was until many years later, when I heard the word "heartburn" and took my first swig of Maalox.

I was depressed at the idea of leaving the womb and obsessed with the idea of staying put. What if the outside world was dangerous and full of pain? *Two minutes B.D. One minute B.D.* Two giant forceps surged at me. They veered to the right; I squirmed to the left. They moved left, and I veered right. Suddenly, they fooled me and feinted as in basketball. The forceps changed directions, and as I turned my head they banged my right eye, leaving a big shiner. Then, they grabbed me and pulled me out, me with my primal scream, and I spent the rest of my life learning how obsessive thoughts shape my shy, disorganized, shleppy behavior.

Born on the sixteenth of June, 1932 "A.D." (After Delivery), and in the depths of the Depression, I had nowhere to go but up. I was predestined to become a stockbroker.

But first, I came out disorganized, disheveled, and a bit *shleppy.*

Dr. Eyerman took a quick look and screamed, "Oh my goodness! This is strange."

My parents were worried. "What's the matter?" my mother asked.

"I've never seen such a black eye coming out of the womb."

"Ah well," Mama said, "at least it's not the evil eye."

"What is it?" my father said.

"I'm not sure," the doctor stuttered.

"Is it a boy?" Pop asked.

"I don't know."

"What do you mean you don't know?" my father screamed.

The doctor turned me over and around, looked at my rear,

and gave me a little twirl.

"It ... it's ... a ... *shlepper.*"

"Are you sure?" my mother asked.

"Could be a *shlemiel*," the doctor said.

"Isn't there a chance it could be a *mensh*?" my father asked.

"We'll have to see how it develops."

I learned later just how much Pop believed in being a *mensh*.

The doctor was right the first time. I was a born *shlepper* who crawled along awkwardly, messily, slowly, like a sloth or a disorganized slob. Later, toddling around the house, I couldn't even keep my diapers on. I always made sure I left a trail so I wouldn't get lost: baby clothes, baby bottles, socks, and, later, tissues, pens, suit coats — anything so I could find my way back.

If being a *shlepper* wasn't bad enough, I also had to face my first slice of life — the *bris* or circumcision ceremony.

The Ecumenical Bris

Ironically, I was born at St. Anthony's Hospital, a venerable old Catholic institution in north St. Louis. Dr. Eyerman, my mother's doctor, though Jewish, had recently moved to Grand Avenue and become associated with the hospital. Thus, my Jewish star would be the first to alight in a room full of crosses. Well, maybe not the first.

Like every Jewish boy, I had to endure the ritual of the *bris*, otherwise known as the circumcision. The nuns were so nervous, I could hear them individually rolling their rosary beads, counting fifty-five Hail Marys. After all, this was to be their first *bris*.

Jews are an optimistic people. Why else would they slice two inches off a boy's *shmeckel*, or penis, before they knew how long it would grow? What if it never healed? Never grew back? I shriveled when I heard that the *mohel* (pronounced *moyel*), otherwise known as a salami-slicing circumciser, coming to cut my itsy-bitsy teenie-weenie. A group of relatives had gathered to watch a meat cutter make chopped liver of my dingdong. I could only imagine what they were going to serve later for refreshments. They all wore *yarmulkas*, or skullcaps, on their heads while the sisters' heads were covered by their habits.

"Call the rabbi. Where's the *mohel*? Surely he couldn't have gotten lost!" someone shouted. I had to find a way out; I had to use my noodle. I began one of my favorite passions to ease the pain — daydreaming about how my *shmeckel* could have been saved. I imagined Abraham might have been casually smoking his favorite Havana cigar when God commanded him to be circumcised. You were probably begatting so many children you were giving out cigars all over the place. That's why you weren't concentrating when God commanded you to cut the tip off your cigar. You thought he meant the stogie dangling down below, the one that Jewish wives have refused to smoke ever since, because they fear they'll burn their tongues. So you took your cigar cutter and clipped your shmeckel. Oy! Oy! Oy! The pain that would be felt throughout the ages. If only you had gotten it straight. Look how I would have been saved all this pain if they were coming to cut my father's Havana cigar. And just think, Castro could have become a rabbi and the first Cuban mohel!

The mohel finally arrived, wearing a tall black hat, a long black beard, and thick glasses. "So this is the boy. My, what a shiny head you have," he said, patting the light bulb in the lamp. The continuous shaking of his right hand, which could have been early Parkinson's disease, horrified me. He bumped into the table and said, "Excuse me!"

I was in a basket, all wrapped up with my schlong sticking up. When I saw the knife, I cringed and squirmed. He pulled out a magnifying glass. Oh, my God! The mohel-rabbi couldn't see straight. Did that mean he also couldn't cut straight?

The rabbi began to chant a *Broche*, or prayer. The ceremony of circumcision takes place on the eighth day after birth because the first seven days refer to the Biblical creation of the natural world. The eighth day is above nature, focusing on the spiritual, with more reliance on God.

"Awmain (amen)," the rabbi shouted with affirmation after the prayer. The others joined in. From the back of the room, a chorus of voices chanted, "Hail, Mary!"

The mohel, with the knife in one hand and his magnifying

glass in the other, drew nearer and nearer. If only I had never left the womb and the forceps had not grabbed me. I felt the same anxiety as when I had said, *Now it's two minutes B.D.* I cringed as the mohel came closer I could only think *Now I'm eight days old, now I'm eight days old.* And the thoughts were growing older.

A giant face with one huge eye, glowing like Cyclops peering at Odysseus, came closer and closer to my limp noodle. I had no spear as Odysseus had to fling at the monster orb, so I willed my first of many erections. When the mohel came within an inch, my hard noodle gave him a big kick in the nose.

"Oy!" he cried as his glasses went flying. But the half-blind mohel was resilient. He put his glasses back on and came at me with a vengeance. With a sudden commotion, a clutch of hands held me down, and the mohel performed the bris. Oy, the pain, the pain as he shortchanged me an inch for the rest of my life. I felt no great lasting effect, but to this day, I can't piss straight.

The knife would always remain fixed in my mind as the unkindest cut of all. I also learned why Judaism was never a proselytizing religion. What *gentile* in his right mind would agree to the pain of circumcision? The Inquisition was bad enough.

The mohel claimed he was innocent. He said I was the one who had moved, not his hand. How could I be guilty when my legal defense was self-defense? Thus ended the first ecumenical bris in history.

"Hallelujah!" sang the nuns.

However, the shaky mohel must have felt guilty. He continues to send me a bottle of skin bracer every year on the anniversary of my bris.

When my parents brought me home the next day, Aaron, my brother, six years older than I, jumped on the running board of my father's 1932 Chevy and greeted me with, "Trow 'em in dah garbage." My parents hesitated for a moment, but then decided to keep me even though I had a terrible red rash on my face. My brother suggested they call me "Leper." The name would have stuck, but once, when I was crying loudly, Mama yelled, "Sha* . . . Sha . . . Leper . . . shh . . .

Shh . . . what'll the neighbors think?" Next time she shortened it to, "Shh-Leper, be quiet." And that's how I came to be known as Shlepper.

* Shut up.

Life on a Tepelleh

After the miserable pain of the *bris*, life as a baby was absolute bliss. My family treated me like royalty — everyone waited on me. Mama and my grandmother washed me, fed me, and wiped my face and rear end.

Leaving my diapers on the floors with my tissues, I reached my first milestone at age thirteen months. In July 1933, I took the first giant step for mankind.

While shlepping through my *Homo Erectus* period, I began to invent a language all my own. As my brother later told me (and that's how I know), I was in dire need of Henry Higgins.

"I want a Donka-Dola," I would say.

"What?" my father would ask. I would point to a bottle of Coca-Cola on the table.

"Oh, a Coke, why didn't you say so in the first place?"

By three years of age I had made vast strides in my elocution. "I'd like a Donka-Dola," and want to go to "Yesson Moyels."

"What's a Yesson Moyel?" my father asked.

"The building in Dorest Dork."

My father had begun to understand my lingo. "Oh, Forest Park. And you want to go to the Jefferson Memorial."

"You dot it."

I loved playing at Yesson Moyel with all the doys and dirls, watching all the tars drive by.

At age four, I ran into my first impediment. I became constipated. To poop or not to poop, that was the question. The urge, unfortunately, came whenever I was in Pop's car.

"Hold it, hold it," he said as we bounded along. "Don't go in the car. What are we going to do?"

My parents came up with a brilliant idea. They bought a *tepelleh* — a small portable wooden toilet. My brother was in charge of carrying the pot. He never forgave me and to this day, he still calls me "Stinky."

All I had to say was, "I gotta go," and everyone was in an uproar.

"Stop the car, stop the car."

"I can't stop the car, I've got to slow down."

"I gotta go."

"Hurry up."

We finally stopped on the side of the street, and Aaron would put down the *tepelleh*.

"Now go fast," my brother urged, "before a car hits you."

So I would discover that life was not always a laughing matter. Sometimes I would find myself in the pits. As the first day of kindergarten approached, so would I soon learn what hell awaited me.

The Little Shlepper.com
Boy or Girl?

THE WICKED WITCH
OF THE WEST

In the peaceful autumn of 1937, while the Hindenberg dirigible was passing the Empire State Building, Amelia Earhart was flying around the world, and the Italians were invading Ethiopia, I was entering the first circle of hell — kindergarten.

Mama took me to Hamilton Elementary School, on Laurel and Westminster streets, in St. Louis. Seeing a huge room with large windows and long shiny floors, I trembled and took my first steps into this new world of enlightenment. But it turned out to be my Dark Ages.

Mama led me to a huge figure, an enormous blimp of a woman. She stood there, her arms outstretched, elbows outward in a Mussolini-ish posture — my kindergarten teacher, Miss Hill. She could have been mistaken for Miss Earhart's plane.

Her steely eyes peered down from her stone face. Mama could say only, "Now behave yourself. This nice teacher will see that you enjoy your first day of school. Don't give her any trouble." Mama ambled off, leaving me with my nemesis.

"Why are you looking down?" the teacher asked.

I was too afraid and shy to look up.

"You'll talk when you're talked to."

"Y-yes."

"Yes, what? You'll say, 'Ma'am.'"

"Y-yes, ma'am."

"Now get your hands out of your pockets."

I pulled them out, and the bunch of tissues I used to blow my nose fell on the floor.

"How could you drop all that toilet paper on my beautiful floors?"

"They're tissues," I said.

The more nervous I felt, the more I needed to repeat things. Instead of: *"Now it's five minutes B.D. (Before Delivery), three minutes B.D."* I had graduated to: *"Now I'm five years old, now I'm five."* While Miss Hill scolded me, I kept repeating, *"Now I'm five, now I'm five. Now I'm five, now I'm five."* All day long these thoughts pounded my little brain, making concentrating more difficult.

"Look up," Miss Hill commanded. I was too busy ruminating to hear her command. Thinking of two things at once would always be a problem for me.

"Look up," she shouted.

"Now I'm five. Now I'm five," I blurted out my secret thought for the first time.

"I didn't ask how old you are."

"Now I'm five, now I'm five."

"I told you to stop that," she said.

I didn't know why I kept saying these things. I got so nervous I raised my head. My stomach quivered and heartburning acid surged into my esophagus. Then I upchucked all over the floor.

"How dare you throw up on my shiny floor!" she said. She went for a mop, and handed it to me. "Hurry up," she said. But I was so slow she finally called the janitor.

Miss Hill ordered us into our little desk chairs, where we had to sit at attention, hands clasped on the desk. If we made noise, she would rap our knuckles with the ruler she always carried in her hand. But the worst was keeping us from going to the bathroom until recess. The kids raised their hands, asking, demanding, begging to make a number one or number two. I squirmed, crossed my legs, holding on for dear life.

Somehow I made it to recess and ran like a gazelle to the bathroom. "*Don't let go, don't let go,*" I said to myself. I couldn't bear the idea of wetting myself — on the fly. I reached the bathroom with barely a second to spare. If I were there today, I would be in deep, deep water.

After leaving kindergarten, I lost track of Miss Hill until *The Wizard of Oz* came out. To my utter shock and disbelief, there she was, my Miss Hill, having lost several hundred pounds, riding her bicycle past the spinning house — the real Wicked Witch of the West.

What's in a Name?

My parents got even for my lengthy delivery by officially naming me Rodowe (pronounced ROD a way) Wesley Fadem II. According to Jewish custom, I should have been named for a deceased relative, but my father, ever grateful to the superintendent of schoolyards, Rodowe Abeken I, for getting him a job during the depths of the Depression, named me after him. I never knew where Wesley came from, perhaps an ecumenical touch from the famous Methodist, John Wesley. What's in a name? Sometimes pain, sometimes fame.

John Fitzgerald Kennedy had the rhythm for success. No one dared make fun of his name. Every September, starting with first grade, I suffered the *oys* and *veys* of outrageous torment from my classmates. On the first day of the school year, the inquisitors of the classroom, led by our teacher, began torturing me.

"Roda . . . Roda . . . What kind of name is . . . Rodowee?" the teacher would ask, laughing.

Then one classmate cried out, "Rodow-O-O-O!"

I cringed and slumped in my chair.

"Rodow-E-E-E!" screamed another.

I slipped lower in my seat as my mood swooped into depression.

Another yelled, "Rudaway!" And finally, "Rodent!" They all started chanting. I slipped further down, hoping to disappear into the molecules of the wood.

At recess, I would run out to the schoolyard, wanting to escape, but immediately I'd hear, "Rhoda." Oh, how the taunting ripped at my heart, my soul, even after Mama gave me the nickname Roddy.

Softball hurled another problem my way. Not seeing straight handicapped my hitting a ball. Worse, we only had seventeen players. So each team captain would take turns choosing sides. Every time we got down to the odd man out, guess who was always left? The *shlepper*.

I was a triple *C* Class *Shlepper* League ballplayer. If I played first base, I overthrew second and third. At third, the ball went through my legs. In the outfield, every fly ball threatened to knock me out, but as a hitter I had no equal, making the *Guinness Book of World Records* with the lowest lifetime batting average: .000.

My problem was my bad right eye. I never saw a ball I couldn't miss. My teammates did the only thing possible — they made me the umpire.

In the fourth grade, the teacher asked me to write the word "news" on the blackboard. When I wrote "swen," she sent me to the school nurse, who called Mama and advised her to take me to the eye doctor.

Covering my left eye, he said, "Now read the top line."

"I don't see a top line," I insisted.

"You don't see a big letter?"

"No. Is that bad?"

"You mean you can't read the *E*? Everyone can read the *E*."

"I can't even see the *E*."

With a special light the doctor peered into my eye. "You've got an amblyopic eye. It never formed correctly." He thoughtfully fitted me with glasses so my schoolmates could call me Four Eyes.

During childhood, when faced with anxiety, I started performing rituals. Some unseen force made me avoid stepping on sidewalk cracks, count when I swallowed water (three gulps every time), and always knock my knuckles on the school desks as I left class. I suppose I thought knocking would bring me luck. When I learned to read, I felt forced to reread everything. While walking, I kept looking back over my shoulder, fearing someone was coming after me. These rituals caused mental chaos in my mind. They desired to control me. I couldn't understand why, but I had a fear that if I didn't do them, something dreadful would happen to me. Why? why? I kept asking myself.

I sought relief from my anxieties in the darkness of the Pageant Theatre, where, on a Sunday afternoon, I saw my first movie, *The Wizard of Oz.* For two hours I found myself transported to a far happier world. That Sunday I began my love affair with movies.

My favorite tough guy was Humphrey Bogart in *Casablanca.* Of course, Bogart, Bergman, and I "would always have Paris."

I loved the film *Lassie, Come Home.* Lassie had beautiful eyes. The collie came from great blood lines and obviously had great genes. Far better than I had.

And then I saw Roddy McDowell, my namesake, petting Lassie. Why couldn't I be on that screen? Why, God, didn't You give me acting genes? Although my alter ego was cute and Lassie had appeal, I quickly tired of them.

Fortunately, the scene changed. Like an irresistibly colorful Renoir painting, the vision of loveliness known as Elizabeth Taylor blew me away. She was so gorgeous and radiated such sexuality that my bag of popcorn, sitting on my lap, exploded. Elizabeth was my age and height, but why, God, did You give her all the beauty genes and me the shleppy ones? How could You make her a goddess and me a *nebbish*?

Why did You give her a face that could launch a thousand ships and me the one that could sink them? She got the lovely Grecian nose, and I Cyrano's. She had the beautiful hair, while mine looked like misused Grecian Formula. She with luminous violet eyes and I with shabby brown. And why should she have such lustrous skin, and me not even foreskin? Look at the exquisite lips, God, the exquisite smile. All You gave me were leftovers.

As we both grew older, she acquired the fragrance "Passion" and I attained the scent of flatulence. Of course, nobody's perfect; You gave her the unstable marriage genes.

I don't mean to complain, but You'll have to admit that You miss-gened me just a bit. In my odyssey through life, couldn't I have called on You to work some miracles for me — even if they were little bitty ones? I must admit that now — fifty years later — You did even the score. Now Liz looks like me. And she's doing all the complaining.

How I Whistled
A Happy Tune

I always looked forward to neighborhood birthday parties and curly paper party blowers with whistles inside. One day, some of us got the idea to pull the small circular tin whistles out of the paper and put them into our mouths. Unfortunately, I blew so hard, it flew out of my mouth. I picked it up to blow again, and disaster struck.

"I swallowed my whistle! I swallowed my whistle!"

Everyone gathered. My heart revved. Oh, my God, where did it go, and how would I get it out? I started crying when my brother organized the kids and they all paraded down the sidewalk to my house and singing, "Roddy swallowed a whiiiistle! Roddy swallowed a whiiiistle!"

Eight children marched, my brother in front, waving his arms as if he had a baton. Duh-de-duh, duh-de-duh, duh-de-duh! Kids pretended to play the flute, the trumpet, or the trombone. My brother was the first Music Man.

"Roddy swallowed a whiiiistle! Roddy swallowed a whiiiistle!" they screeched. And there, dragging up the line was the poor little *shlepper* — me — crying, fearing I would be whistling through my ass for the rest of my life.

Hearing the momentous news, Mama sobbed, "What are we going to do?" Pop was calm. "It's only a little whistle."

Through the window I still heard, "Roddy swallowed a whistle." I expected a radio report at any moment.

"Oh, my Roddy," Mama said.

"Press his belly button," my brother volunteered.

"Call Dr. Eyerman," Mama said.

"Call the *mohel*," my brother offered.

"Wrong end," I said.

The doctor said to observe me for several days, and if I experienced pain or blockage, take me to the hospital for exploratory surgery. I ran to the refrigerator, stuffed myself with cherries, peaches, watermelon, honeydew, and several squares of the most popular chocolate laxative of the day — Ex-Lax.

A half-hour later, I announced: "I've got my whistle back." But I never blew it again. At least I had found a cure for anal retentiveness.

THE BATTLE OF
THE BALLOONS

As I approached my eighth birthday in June 1940, I first acknowledged my need to dwell on things, whether repetitive thoughts or a complete preoccupation with a subject like the grim news coming out of Europe.

I read all the headlines, and every week at the movies I watched the newsreels of World War II, especially the Battle of Britain. With gleeful excitement, I observed the aerial war between the British R.A.F. and the German Luftwaffe. The fighter planes soared and dove at each other, firing in slashing staccato bursts the machine guns set in their wings. My exhilaration mounted as each plane tried to outmaneuver the other until one plane exploded into a ball of fire and plummeted to the sea.

Inspired, I blew up my own balloons until they popped, pretending I was shooting down the Messerschmitt fighters, pop, pop, pop, all over London. But I was really living at 5782 Kingsbury, near De Baliviere Avenue in St. Louis, and the old Wintergarden skating rink. Our house was a typical six-family apartment building, run down and decrepit. How could I know we were poor when I always had three meals a day, and a dime to go to the Pageant movie theater on Sunday afternoons?

Naturally, when my mother shared her plans for my birthday party, I told her I wanted a clown who could twist balloons into the shape of airplanes. Fortunately, she had heard of a balloon-blowing girl, a bozo who was way ahead of her time. Mama hired her for a dollar.

The clown arrived in yellow polka dots and a dunce cap. She turned her balloons into salami-like airplanes, which we threw into the air, yelling, "Rat-a-tat-tat," as we tried to shoot them down.

Mama served kosher hot dogs, potato chips, Donka-Dolas, and whistle blowers. (I had learned my lesson.) In the backyard, the clown drew a circle in the gravel for a dart game. In the center of the circle, a used milk carton served as the target. Everyone gathered while I took careful aim. Considering wind velocity, temperature, and gravitation, I threw the dart in the air in a scientifically calibrated arc. The dart rose, slowly descended and disappeared.

"Where'd it go?" someone asked.

"It's gone with the wind."

Morton Simon, who stood directly opposite me, searched everywhere when suddenly, I noticed the dart sticking out of his left shin bone, a minor wound. Some kids screamed, but how much could it have hurt? He didn't even cry. But my father, looking unusually distressed, drove Morton to the hospital.

Meanwhile, I stayed home and couldn't wait for my next turn. For some reason, everyone ran when I picked up the second dart. All the kids hid in the house.

I followed them inside, where the clown pointed out the wall where we would play "Pin the Tail on the Donkey."

She had me close my eyes and blindfolded me. A big mistake.

I walked slowly through the darkness with everyone scurrying away. Finally, I stuck the pin, not exactly on the donkey, but on my cousin Don's right eyelid.

Oh, the screaming as an ambulance packed him off to the hospital. The nerve! He could still see better than I could. I started running around, popping all the balloons.

Everyone ran out, knocking over tables and chairs, escaping.

I had a marvelous time. Morton and Don didn't talk to me for five years, and I couldn't understand why fewer and fewer kids showed up at my subsequent birthday parties. I grew so desperate, I had to bribe those who came with my best marbles.

At the movies the next week, I saw an English Spitfire's wing blown off, the wounded plane spiraling out of control and belching smoke all the way down, down, down. For the first time, I realized the horror of war and what the Spitfire's pilot, a fellow human being, faced.

Emerging from darkness with a new vision, I no longer experienced the excitement of war, but rather the utter devastation of its victims. Each night, I curled up on the living-room couch and listened to Walter Winchell, the most popular reporter of the era, pressing the telegraph on his desk.

Dot… dot… dot. "Good evening, Mr. and Mrs. America. Let's go to press, page one. The Battle of Britain has entered a new phase. Herr Hitler has ordered the vengeful, unrelenting bombing of London."

I would follow the war for the duration, but as for my backyard air battles, my fantasies went poof.

Pop, Aaron and me — 1938
Notice how the shlepper is always looking down.

"Doddy Doves Deddity"

(Roddy Loves Beverly)

✍

I drank a lot of Dunka Dolas the next year, before I learned the King's English. The next summer, I first noticed Beverly, my next-door neighbor, who was a little blonde with the cutest smile. For the first time, I felt this new, delicious feeling of infatuation, a combination of fondness and longing. Was this the meaning of that word I kept hearing on the radio and the movies — "What is this thing called love?"

My serene bliss ended abruptly when my brother, as was his custom, made fun of my difficulties with the English language by composing a little ditty:

"Doddy doves Deddity."

"Doddy doves Deddity"

I had my first crush. The good news was that I couldn't get her and her beautiful smile out of my head.

The bad news: this new obsession called love vied with other repetitions in my mind, which had expanded to *Now I'm five. Now I'm nine,* and counting, *one, two, three, four, three, two, one.* For a while, my new obsession clobbered the old ones, almost crowding them out.

Unfortunately, I was so shy, I could hardly talk to Beverly. I could only gaze longingly out the back window and watch her play by the oak tree.

To myself, I repeated my brother's chant *Doddy doves Deddity, Doddy doves Deddity.* New repetitions fought with existing ones. What was this thing called love? Could it be associated with what I heard someone call the facts of life?

What was this new feeling of exhilaration I felt between my loins? Like most kids, I was coming to terms with my sexuality, and I was totally confused. Could Beverly be part of the puzzle, otherwise known as the facts of life?

I decided to get the straight dope from the only person I knew who could offer it — Mama.

How I Learned
To Be Fruitful

*"*Mommy, where did I come from?"

Without a moment's hesitation, she said, "I cut open a cantaloupe and out you popped."

"From a cantaloupe?"

"That's right."

As if on cue, she cut up a cantaloupe and served me a slice. I found it unsettling because I had the feeling I was eating myself. This revelation had no lasting effect, but for ten years I thought I was a fruit. I soon deduced that other fruits bore different offspring: fat girls must have come from watermelons, thin girls from bananas. The real beauties came from peaches. That's how I learned to be fruitful and multiply.

In all my years at home, my parents never used the word sex. Their only concession to sexuality was an occasional, "The stork delivered a baby."

My parents continually bickered about me. My mother had wanted a girl, so she dressed me in effeminate baby clothes and let my hair grow into long curls. Looking at a photograph of me as a four-year-old, I saw an unbelievably cute little girl with a Bob Hope slope of a nose. I should have had a clue at the *bris*. Looking at the picture, I can only feel a question mark down below. Although aware of a dangling participle between my legs, years would pass before I discovered why my question mark would suddenly stiffen into an exclamation point.

I couldn't believe Mama was giving me the straight dope. I

loved cantaloupes, but had no desire for them. My only obsession was with Doddy doves Deddity. How sweet the words still lie in my memory. But several years would pass before I learned how I was born. And it would be in the most unexpected place.

WHAT I DID FOR
THE WAR EFFORT

Little did I know that one obsession would disappear, only to be replaced by another. I realized this when I once more gazed through the back window at Beverly, while listening to the radio — *Orson Welles Mercury Theatre.* A sudden silence on the radio woke me from my daydreaming. Then came:

"This is the Mutual Broadcasting System. Ladies and gentlemen, we interrupt this broadcast to bring you an important bulletin. Flash! Washington — The White House has announced a Japanese attack on Pearl Harbor."

I felt a chill, and heard a lot of talk among some relatives who had stopped by. "Not another war after all these years!" Pop said.

"At least we shot down twenty-nine of their planes," Mama said.

I could only ask: "Why would anyone bomb a pearl in a harbor?" I had to find it on the map. I read every word in the newspapers about the fall of Wake Island, the Bataan death march, Guadalcanal, and the battle for North Africa.

Everyone was united in winning the war. The war news was so bleak, I took it to my heart. A heaviness and coldness settled in my chest that I would someday recognize as depression. At the time, who knew what I had or why? Other kids in school didn't seem to worry about this battle for the world.

A map on the front page of the *St. Louis Post-Dispatch* showed the Nazis' penetration to the heart of Russia. I looked up Russia in our old used Encyclopaedia Britannica, and found it was one huge country. I read how Napoleon had invaded Russia in 1812 and would have won, had the winter not defeated him.

I became fascinated with Napoleon, especially when I read that he was a screw-up and all the kids made fun of his awkwardness in cadet school. He was no soldier, but obviously a great general. Reading about him inspired me. He would turn out to be my hero, but he made one big mistake: he invaded Russia.

I asked the teacher if I could put up a map of Europe and follow the Eastern front. She agreed, and I used a yellow string held fast by thumbtacks to represent my arrow: through Minsk, Kiev, Rostov, all the way to the crucial battle of the war, the house-to-house fighting at Stalingrad.

Winter hit St. Louis hard and I trudged, freezing, every morning through the snow. I got sick with the flu and had to stay home. I missed my map and began to wonder if the weather was frigid here, what could it be like in Stalingrad? It would be 1812 all over again. This was the first time I realized my potential as a military strategist.

What started as a cough that harsh winter turned into a fever. Dr. Eyerman, the doctor who delivered me, made a house call. (Yes, doctors actually made house calls in those days.) He looked like a rotund Santa Claus with white whiskers. I expected a "ho, ho, how are you?" But all I heard was, "You got a shot of schnaaps, Mike?" My father obliged and they had a friendly drink of whiskey. He finally came over to my bed and asked me where I hurt.

I pointed to my chest.

With two fingers, he thumped my chest cavity. "That's it," he said.

"What's it?" asked my father.

"He's still a *shlepper*, but he's got pneumonia."

How could the doctor, without using X-rays or taking me to

the hospital, tell I had this dangerous disease by just using two fingers? Well, maybe it's not so strange when nowadays, you see doctors checking the prostate with one finger and sometimes two, if a second opinion is needed.

The word "pneumonia" sounded vile and scared me. Mama cried, which scared me more. Fears of death pulsated through my mind, and only new repetitive words calmed me: *Flu, pneumonia, flu, pneumonia.*

I was home for six weeks, swallowing the most vile-tasting sulfa drug, white powder poured into water. Since I didn't die, the ritual wordplay must have worked again.

Feeling better, I returned to school, where I discovered that the Germans must have been sick, too. The winter had struck them down and finally I moved the yellow string two inches to the west. The Germans were retreating from Stalingrad in the snow on the long road back to Berlin. "The Russians are winning! The Russians are winning!" I yelled.

The other kids greeted my startling announcement with a yawn. I had called the turn in the war and nobody cared. Even President Roosevelt didn't call me. I sure could have taken a lot of weight off his shoulders.

THE HEBREW SCHOOL CAPTIVITY

After the *bris*, the second most painful experience for a Jewish boy is going to *chedar* or Hebrew school. Everyone I knew hated Hebrew school. In fact, in my whole adult life, I have never met anyone who liked Hebrew school, even a rabbi whom I met decades later.

My parents wanted me to be a super Jew. My mother thought I should be orthodox; my father, reform. This was common during the thirties and the forties. Perhaps parents wanted to give their children the best of both worlds. So I shlepped to the orthodox Miriam Hebrew School every weekday after school, to the orthodox Sheri Tellem Synagogue on Saturday mornings, and to B'nai El Temple, a reform house of worship on Sundays.

The quintessential ambivalent Jew, when faced with the difficulties of orthodoxy and easiness of reform, I would choose, like millions of others, the easy way — reform Judaism.

After grammar school as I traipsed through the streets and alleys to Hebrew school, I would hear the radios through the open windows of the apartments:

"Corregidor holds on the forty-ninth straight day. . ."

"Oxydol presents, *Ma Perkins.*

"It's time for *The Young Widow Brown* and her search for love."

"And now, *The Romance of Helen Trent,* the program that asks the question: 'Can a woman over thirty-five find romance?'"

But the most zestful window of all was Mama's, where the aroma of my grandmother, Bubbe's freshly baked onion rolls was enough to make my stomach gurgle.

I made my way to De Baliviere and turned past Wolff-Wolffie's drugstore, where occasionally I would buy a three-scoop ice cream cone for five cents, and then past J. Sokolnick's grocery store. Arriving at 5744 Waterman, I trudged up the cracked steps of the two-story building, which housed our Hebrew school. There stood Meyer Schwab, our Hebrew schoolteacher. He was tall and slender and had a sad and lonely look. His mournful eyelids shadowed his deep-set gray eyes. His nose was angular, his visage stern. Perhaps his most illuminating trait was that he never smiled.

His clothes were slovenly and worn out, with a few burn marks on his suit jacket. This undoubtedly came from smoking cigarettes down to the butt, then letting the ashes settle all over him. To our everlasting shame, we made fun of him with a cacophony of yelling, joking, whistling and jostling. At the time, none of us had any idea he had spent time in the Dachau concentration camp before the war. What did we know? We thought Hebrew school epitomized suffering.

"*Sha**" shouted Meyer Schwab. We greeted his command with more noise, and shoving, we threw pencils at each other.

"*Sha! Sha!*" Meyer screamed. "Are you animals or human beings?"

He grabbed the ruler on the desk and slapped it against his own hand, glaring at us until we got the message. For the moment only, we listened intently.

Meyer announced we would read the *Five Books of Moses* and, after we finished at the end of the year, we would have a party with candy and soda pop.

We also learned about all the colorful Biblical characters who came after the time of Moses. I could imagine myself as King David, beating the odds of humble beginnings and trouncing the

---

* Shut up.

giant, Goliath, with a single stone. I longed to be like Samson, strong, handsome and virile. If only I could find a beautiful Delilah, but I refused to lose my hair to her.

When we came to the psalms of David, especially the Twenty-Third Psalm — the kids were fooling around. I, as usual, daydreamed.

Meyer Schwab spoke, "Thy rod and thy staff they comfort me — "

Rod? I awoke with a start. Was someone calling me?

"He restoreth my soul."

Was the Lord sending me a message? Was he talking to my soul? Would I someday understand?

The teacher stood on his toes, singing, "*Kadosh, Kadosh, Kadosh,* holy, holy, holy is the Lord of Hosts. When we pray to the angels we stand on our toes to be closer to them. When we invoke the Kadosh we imitate the angels who float upward to sanctify God." Was it possible to believe in something, like angels, that we could not see?

The kids all continued talking and joking. With the veins bulging in his forehead, Meyer snatched his ruler and violently slammed it on his desk. "You're here to learn the tenets of your faith, the essence of Judaism that you will live by all of your life. The first prayer you will learn is the Shma."

He began chanting "*ShmaYisrael.*" He raised his voice from minor to major key, singing, "*Adonoy Elohenu*" and then closed forcefully with, "*Adonoy ECHAD*" (Here, O' Israel, the Lord, our God, the Lord is One).

"Say this prayer when you rise in the morning, the last thing before you go to bed, and before you die. Your life will be filled, the good and the bad, but no matter how terrible, if you return to God, you will live in peace again."

He kept talking, but we never listened.

The next afternoon, I again trudged from school past Laurel

Avenue into the alley behind 5782 Kingsbury. The same radio soap operas were emanating from each open window. *Young Widow Brown* was still searching for a husband when I heard, "We interrupt this program to bring you this bulletin. Warm Springs, Georgia. President Roosevelt is dead. I repeat, President Roosevelt has died of a stroke."

A thought intruded. *Kiss of death, kiss of death.*

I was shocked. It couldn't be. He was our leader. At that moment, I could feel a cold hush in the area. When I reached De Baliviere Avenue, I picked up a Post-Dispatch for three cents and treaded lightly up the steps to Hebrew school class. There, sitting forlornly on his chair, his head in his arms, was Meyer Schwab.

"He can't be dead," he said. "He's the only hope for the Jews of the world." He saw my afternoon paper and grabbed it. "See, there is no mention of Roosevelt dying. It couldn't be."

I tried to comfort him and myself as the repetitive thought kept striking my mind: *Kiss of death, kiss of death.* I could only try to assuage my anxieties with: *Kiss of life, kiss of life.*

Mom And Pop

"Love at First Fight"

~∂~

Mama and Pop were the funniest parents anyone could ever have had. They were a combination of *Burns and Allen* and *Fibber Mcgee and Molly* of the golden age of radio.

My mother, in her prime, was an attractive, high-cheekboned brunette. Supposedly the best dancer in St. Louis in 1917, she dubbed herself the belle of the ball. Her dance card always filled up first, she loved to tell us. Mama wore Parisian perfume that smelled of gardenias. You could smell it from twenty paces. But mostly I remember her as someone who walked excruciatingly slow. She *shlepped* along, enveloped in another world.

The eldest of three sisters, Mama was the last to marry. Bubbe, in a self-fulfilling prophesy, was so worried about Mama's ability to cook and clean, that she did all the household chores. So Mama never learned.

Pop always sported a bow tie. Tall and well-dressed, slender, with a receding hairline and a thin mustache, he walked quickly. Holding himself erect, he never forgot he was a U.S. Marine. Mama plodded behind him.

"Honey, march faster!" he commanded.

"Can't you go slower, Mickey? My feet hurt," she complained.

"Honey, get yourself some marching shoes."

His marine picture showed him proud in his blue uniform, his medals on his chest. Though I long thought he won the Purple Heart in combat in France, it turned out that a kick in the rear by a mule in Mexico earned him the Purple Toches (rear end) award.

Beneath a tough exterior, Pop was all heart. My brother told me years later that in 1922, Pop had promised my mother to take care of her own widowed mother for the rest of Bubbe's life. When Pop insisted on putting it in writing, Mama cried. In the 1930s, when Pop got a job at city hall, he helped all his friends get their traffic tickets fixed. No matter how little he had to give monetarily, he always helped people in need.

Mama and Pop were two people living on different planets, which proves that opposites attract. They met providentially on a cold March day in 1922 on a blind date at the downtown Stix, Baer & Fuller Tea Room in St. Louis. Mama ordered cheesecake and tea for the then-enormous price of $1.35.

"One dollar, thirty-five cents!" Pop reportedly yelled, almost choking. "Rose, how could you do that to me? Money doesn't grow on trees! I could buy the same dessert for thirty-five cents just around the corner!"

"But it's Sunday. It's a special day!" Mama said as she tried to get up, slipped, and fell off the chair. Pop, begrudgingly, helped her up.

Mama glided along until they reached the elevator, which, for some unknown reason she knew had a vendetta against her. As if on cue, the elevator stopped two inches below the floor level, and, as usual, she stumbled.

"Do you always trip over yourself, Rose?" Pop said, grabbing her.

"Oh no, only on special occasions. It isn't my fault. Elevators don't seem to like me."

"Look," Pop moaned, "I can't go around picking you up all the time."

Amazingly, a second date followed. My mother made a special meal, a five-course dinner that no five-star restaurant could have matched.

HORS D'OEUVRES

"This chopped liver is really very good," my father said, licking his plate. (Her best dish, she made it by adding *schmaltz*, or chicken fat.)

SOUP:

"You know, Rose, this could use a little something. Could you pass the salt? Would you mind passing the pepper? You know, it could use some mustard, too. Are you sure you didn't put too much water in it?"

ENTREE:

"*Feh!* (Spitting out a mouthful.) This chicken is dry and hairy. And the mashed potatoes, I've never seen so many lumps. And the corn, stringy. I can't get the crap out of my teeth."

"I'm sorry you don't like it," my mother said, bewildered.

"Damn it, Rose!" my father ranted. "I thought you said you could cook!" Thus, the bickering began.

But a miracle occurred on the third date. They got engaged. This was love at first fight.

How Mama Drove
Pop Crazy

$\mathcal{L}\mathcal{O}$

While growing up, I barely knew of these good deeds, or *mitzvahs*, Pop performed. But he wasn't a saint. He got annoyed with my mother's cooking, her *shlepping*, and her depressive moods swings. He constantly bickered with her at the dinner table.

Mama retaliated by joking about Pop's ethnic nose. She would say, "Mickey, with your *Yiddishe* nose, you'll never get into the best hotels." And at night, she wasn't enamored of his nose, either. All I could hear from my adjoining bedroom was: "Mickey, you're snoring!"

"Why don't you get some earplugs?" he would retort.

The Great Depression bulldozed my parents. My father's timing, as always, was bad; he was a stockbroker from 1930-1933. His stocks and mutual funds on average dropped ninety percent. He never made a dime and had to leave for another job, which could not have been worse.

Mama was proud of her Jewishness and thought being one of the Chosen People a blessing. Of course, the gentiles never quite saw it her way. When she and Pop would drive to Florida and go through a small town in Georgia of perhaps five thousand people, she would become the first Jewish evangelist.

Entering a small restaurant, she would say to the owner, "We're Jewish. We're the Chosen People, you know."

The owner would stand there in a T-shirt stretched over a protruding belly, with a cigarette dangling from his lower lip, and a puzzled look on his face. "I don't reckon I've ever seen Jew folk before. What do they *dew-w*? I always thought they had horns on their heads," he said.

"Honey." My father would give her a little shove. "Can't you keep your mouth shut?" Then he'd whisper, "They're liable to lynch us. Let's get out of here."

Mama meant well, but when it came to religion, Mama was not very tolerant. She hated *shiksehs*, or gentile girls. They weren't good enough for her Jewish boys. Somehow, she got the idea that Aaron was dating *shiksehs*, probably because he always came back from a date feeling so happy. One evening, he was talking on the phone to a girl named Catherine. Without warning, my mother ran up and yelled into the receiver, "Dirty, lousy *shikseh*!"

My brother shuddered with embarrassment. "Ma, she's only typing my term paper."

Mama saved everything. She was a hoarder, and she also did repetitive things. She wore her old clothes over and over in order to save her one new dress. She put rugs atop rugs to save the original rugs, and newspapers on rugs to save the rug covers. In 1941, I could read all about the German invasion of Russia on my way to the living room, and I could catch up with the funnies and Joe DiMaggio's fifty-six-game hitting streak by the time I reached the dining room. I never knew the color of the sofa because it was covered with furniture throws, otherwise known as *shmattehs*. She also talked to herself, a kind of repetitive mumbling. I wondered if she suffered from the same problems I did.

Mama bought all her shoes on sale, even if they were the wrong size. She saved dirty soap water and already perked coffee grounds in jars under the sink, all for reuse. She kept a veritable storehouse of energy for us, a bottle of *schmaltz*, in the refrigerator. She would continually cook with it. But to spread it on *challah* (wonderful baked bread) was pure pleasure. Putting schmaltz toast in your mouth was like eating pure energy fat, energy that went straight to your body so you hardly needed a coat in winter. The fat that went straight to your arteries. During the cold nights of the thirties, I didn't even need a blanket; my continual heartburn kept me warm.

Mama specialized in driving my pop crazy. Take the day when she started chilling her cold cream in the refrigerator. She spooned it into a used container of Smetana brand sour cream. Whenever she needed to refresh her face, she applied the cold cold cream.

One evening, I watched my father (who always had a craving for sour cream) enter the kitchen. He opened the refrigerator and reached for the Smetana.

"Stop! Stop!" I screamed. But it was too late. He put a tablespoonful of face moisturizer in his mouth.

"Whooosh! Phhhhh! Phhhhh!" His cheeks bulged and with horror in his eyes, he raced to the sink and spit it out.

"Goddamn it, Honey! What the hell did you put in that container?" he screamed.

"It was only my cold cream."

"But who puts cold cream in a damn Smetana container?"

"It's the only one I could find. I didn't think you'd eat it."

"That is the trouble with you, Honey. You don't think." From then on, Pop never ate Smetana, and my mother used only warm cold cream.

My grandmother, who lived with us, did a lot of the cooking. Unfortunately, when she died, all of Pop's favorite meals passed with her. After the funeral, Pop took my mother by the hand and said, "Honey, I'd like to show you an important room in the house. It's called the kitchen."

But she couldn't make a meal without my father complaining. One night, Mama served us her version of Bubbe's roast beef. After one bite, Pop muttered, "What kind of roast beef is this? It tastes like rubber." Mama froze, saying nothing.

I chewed and chewed, but I could make little headway. I cut

small pieces and gulped them down.

"I know what it is," Pop said, spitting it out. "It's tongue. I hate tongue. You never know where the cows have been licking."

"Ugh," my brother and I blurted out.

"I thought you'd like it, Mickey," poor Mama said. She just liked saving money. Tongue was far cheaper than roast beef.

Pop started making his own special dishes. His favorite was anything not Kosher. And then came that infamous day when my father brought a ham to my still Orthodox mother. "A ham! Mickey!" she said in tears. "What did I ever do to you?"

"You never learned to cook." Out went the kosher brisket, and in came the pork: bacon, chops, even pig's knuckles. When faced with such dire news, my mother could only use her favorite expression: "If you ain't got anything, you ain't got nothing."

From that day on, we switched from Orthodox to Reform Judaism, and Pop was in charge of the kitchen.

Pop had a pepper obsession. His favorite dish was pepper, surrounded by egg, chili, and corn.

"Mickey, why do you have to put corn in the chili?" my mother would say.

"Because I like it, Honey," he said. "No one's asking you to eat it."

Naturally, we began eating out more. If it was a new restaurant, Pop always had trouble finding the place.

"Mickey, ask someone for directions," Mama would say. But Pop, the marine, took no orders from civilians, so we would go up and down almost every street in the vicinity of the restaurant, but rarely the right one.

"There it is!" he would say triumphantly as he accidentally turned onto the right street.

During dinner, the focus of attention was always Aaron. If he was the star in the universe, I was the black hole — shy, introverted, quietly observing everything, retreating into myself.

It wasn't that I was not loved. I was just not the prime focus of my parents' expectations.

"Roddy!" Mama said, "Why don't you eat like Aaron? You know, they're starving in Europe."

Aaron ate so much that I thought soon the whole world would be starving.

"*Ess, ess* (eat, eat) the fish," my mother urged me. "It's brain food. You (pointing directly at me) need it."

Mama loved Sunday mornings. She thought the world was waiting for her to call and invite her and Pop over.

"Do you mind if we stop over this afternoon, Lena?" Cousin Lena was known as the best cook in St. Louis. "Yes, we'll stop by for just a little visit," said Mama.

Keeping on the old clothes she wore around the house, she took out her "new" dress, which she had bought four years before, and folded it neatly in a bag with her favorite "new" shoes, still in the box. Mama and Pop always arrived at 5 P.M., just in time for Sunday dinner and Mama would march herself straight into the bathroom as the original bag lady and come out as the elegant mooch. But her clothes never wore out.

"Here we are. We're so glad to see you."

Pop didn't approve of *shnoring*, begging or mooching off a friend or relative, but he only protested mildly. How much could he object to his only great meal for the week? After dinner, he relaxed, lit a cigar, poured himself a drink of Lena's bourbon, and fell asleep.

Mama was happy in her Sunday clothes and could only say, "Mickey, you're snoring." Lena and her husband glanced at each other, knowing full well they'd been had again. Meanwhile, Mama was busy thinking over next week's victim, humming to herself, "Whom can I *shnore* to?"

And that's how I remember Mama and Pop. No matter what Mama did, from informing the world about the Chosen People to storing cold cream in the refrigerator, she was living as Alice in her own wonderland. She simply and regularly got on Pop's nerves, and he regularly reacted like a military man. Pop, however, showed he cared. Otherwise, why would he always call her "Honey" before he blasted her?

Pop and Mom
Notice how Mama is wearing her everlasting party dress, that she put on
only after arriving at an affair, using the bathroom as a dressing room.

Chocolate Cain

Mama sometimes amazed me. Although she never liked to cook, she loved to bake chocolate cake. Not just any chocolate cake, but a moist, succulent, mouth-watering one. Whenever I heard the mixer roar, my taste buds bloomed.

I would stick my fingers into the bowl and devour a fistful of rich batter. "You're ruining the cake," my brother would protest.

Impatiently counting the minutes, I waited for the cake to bake and Mama to take out her wide knife and cut the first piece.

I was tasting the exquisite sweet chocolate when suddenly, like the fear that engulfed me at my *bris* at the sight of the knife, a horrifying, intrusive thought pained me.

Grab the knife and stab your brother. Grab the knife and —

Shocked, I threw down the cake.

"Roddy, why? Don't you like it? You always loved it."

I stared at the knife, trembling. I ran out of the kitchen and jumped onto my bed.

Kiss of death, kiss of life, kiss of death, kiss of life. New phrases possessed my head. How could I think such thoughts? Guilt, guilt, guilt swamped my mind.

My mother followed me, screaming, "Roddy, what's the matter? What's the matter?"

How could I tell her? The shame. The isolation. I couldn't tell anyone about these horrible thoughts. I could only retreat into my soul, hiding my pain from the world.

How could I tell her that her little Roddy wanted to pick up the knife, not the piece of cake? I buried my head. *Kiss of death, kiss of life.*

New thoughts crowded in every day, trying to force out my

normal thoughts. *Kiss of death, kiss of life, kiss of death, kiss of life, life, life. Ten, nine, eight, seven, six, five, four, three, two, one, two, three, four, five. nine, eight, seven.* The thoughts were pulverizing my mind, making it more and more difficult to concentrate.

From that time on, I would often dive onto my bed when the repetitive thoughts overwhelmed me. My brother's narrow twin bed was next to mine, and I would stick my head between the two, pressing the beds together like a vise around my head. I wanted desperately to contain the horrendous thoughts and crush them into oblivion.

What if I ever acted on such hellish thoughts? How could I be sure I never would? Who would prevent me from having such thoughts? Was I my brother's keeper?

I knew that someday I would have to control this mysterious force. Otherwise, how could I ever forget the bitter taste of chocolate?

ᴌℴ

Could I stop these repetitive thoughts?

One afternoon while walking home from school, I decided to stop the thoughts cold. *Now I'm five, now I'm ten, now I'm five, now —*

Stop, stop. Hold firm. Five seconds, ten, fifteen, twenty. The pressure mounted. I created a vacuum in my mind, a nothingness. I tensed the muscles in my face and my forehead, hoping they would press down on my thoughts. Thirty seconds, forty seconds, forty-two excruciating seconds. The force began pounding, pounding every part of my cranium. My eyes began to bulge. Forty-five seconds and I exploded and poured out: *KISS OF DEATH, KISS OF LIFE, NOW I'M FIVE, TEN, FOUR, THREE, TWO, ONE, TWO, THREE, FOUR, TWO, ONE.*

I could not stop.

Bubbe

On the living room wall hung a large oval black-and-white photograph of my cherished grandmother, Mema Dena Sender, or Bubbe, marked "1900, Warsaw."

I looked at her picture every evening when I walked into the apartment. She had soft black hair combed back in a bun, while in front, short bangs curled. Her face was angular, her skin smooth. Small hoop earrings hung from her earlobes. Her dark eyes gazed out brightly.

In the picture she wore a gray dress with a ruffled neckline and a brooch.

She was always kind to me, helping to rear, clean, feed, and nurture me. As I grew up, I realized the Bubbe always in the kitchen, was no longer reflected in the portrait. My Bubbe was fading. She wore *shmattes* (rags), and stockings with runs. She walked slowly, her facial skin became wrinkled and crepey. Her silver-white hair was still combed in a bun. But what bothered me most was her hands, once lovely I was sure, but now gnarled and knobby.

Bubbe and her husband, Abraham, had immigrated from a small village in Poland that has long since been erased by history. "Life was tough, very tough in Poland," she often said. And it would get tougher. The virulent anti-Semitism of the time would mushroom into an evil cloud forty years later.

She liked to talk about how Abraham had a store on Eighteenth and Pine Streets and was without a doubt the finest tailor in St. Louis. She told us about the loud pounding and digging down the street when workmen built the now famous Union Station at the turn of the century. She was proud of her three daughters, Lilly, Fritzie, and Rosie, whom she frequently took to the fabulous 1904 World's Fair, where the world's first ice cream cones were served.

After being widowed in 1920, she moved in with my parents and helped raise my brother and me. Bubbe always said, referring to my mother, "I had all the girls and Rosie had all the boys. Poor Rosie. She always wanted a little girl." The statement startled me. That's why mama had let my hair grow into long, drooping curls. She wanted me to be the girl she never had!

In addition to doing the cooking, Bubbe was the babysitter for the six-family apartment house where we lived. She sat for Deddity, who lived on the first floor and another girl from the second floor. When their parents left them off, she was not only a babysitter, but a confidant and advisor. One girl's relatives lived in Chicago, so Bubbe became the surrogate grandmother of love and kindness.

Her maladies did not keep her from her beloved kitchen. Though penniless, she wanted to pay her way as a cook. Mama was happy because she liked taking afternoon naps. Pop salivated as he smelled Grandma's matzah-ball soup, roast beef, chicken soup, and best of all, baked *challa* — enough to make your stomach growl.

At Purim time, we all worshiped Bubbe's *hamantashen*, dough baked in a triangle and stuffed with apricots, poppy seeds, or cherries. The triangle, represented the three-cornered hat of the evil Haman who tried to hang all the Jews in Persia, as described in the book of Esther. I couldn't understand how such a tasty morsel could represent such an evil person.

Bubbe couldn't read or write, and therefore, all her recipes remained in her head and out of Mama's.

I spied, one day, a strange phenomenon — forks, knives, and spoons seemingly growing out of the dirt of the potted plants on the windowsill. This is where they come from, plants? No, just

Bubbe's Jewish tradition of placing kitchen utensils in the dirt whenever a mistake was made between the *flayshedik* utensils (for meat) and the *milchedik* ones (for dairy). The tradition would last as long as my grandmother lived. Word of her culinary delights spread throughout the neighborhood. After Hebrew school, a half-block away, I could smell her greatest work of art, the onion rolls. The aroma wafted, titillating my olfactory nerves. In good weather the windows were always open.

Her onion rolls were so warm, moist, and tasty that I could feel my stomach applauding every bite. All the kids came running, the cats and dogs scampering after them. She gave out as many rolls as she could, always with a kind smile. Had we only opened a bakery, we could have become rich.

One winter Bubbe cooked less, and her world shrank. The center of her life became her small bedroom in the front of the house. I heard my parents whisper, "heart trouble."

She had what we now call angina attacks, or "spells" in those days. She would take her red medicine and stay up all night. By morning, she usually felt better.

But one morning she seemed worse. She was going downhill — fast. I raced to the Hamilton schoolyard, where I stopped squarely on homeplate. I stomped my feet over and over again, counting *one, two, three… Twenty-two… Thirty-two,* until I reached one hundred. Magically, Bubbe would live to be one hundred, only if I kept stomping.

When I finally returned home, exhausted, my grandmother appeared to be sleeping. I went to bed, still counting. In the morning I discovered she had died. Bubbe was eighty-two.

Grief was a foreign country for me. I sobbed all day and throughout the funeral. That evening, Bubbe's eyes still shone brightly in her photo. That's how I would always remember her. An intrusive thought kept pounding my brain — *ninety-seven, ninety-eight, ninety-nine* …What if I had counted more?

Bubbe

THE MOCKINGBIRD
OF HEBREW CLASS

For several months after my Bubbe died, I felt cold and somber. Although I fell into a darkening abyss, I found my first coping mechanism that could bring me out of the melancholy hole — humor. I found I could never feel depressed when I laughed.

I craved humor like a woman yearns for the greatest markdown sale at Neiman Marcus. So my depression would lift in the most unlikely of places, Hebrew school, where I learned about sex.

I arrived at school every afternoon where Meyer Schwab, as usual, could not control this bunch of wild Jewish Indians. Meyer shouted, "If you don't shut up, I'll throw you all out, *right away.*"

I, looking down as usual half asleep, jumped up crying, "Yes, yes, I'm here!" I thought he was yelling, "Rodowe."

But Meyer never kept his word and never expelled anyone until he ran into Dov Goldman. Dov was a tall boy, with his *yarmulka* (prayer cap) on a crest of brown hair coming over his forehead. With Dov's beady eyes and aquiline nose, he resembled a bird. He sang like a bird and was an exceptional ventriloquist. The whole class burst out laughing at the chirpings of parrots, crows, and macaws that were always at his beak and call. He was the mockingbird of the classroom, able to mock anything. Dov was at his best when he imitated the school buzzer, which signaled the end of school at 5 P.M. At about a quarter of, he said, "Bzzzzzzzzzzzzzzzzz! Class over!" He leaped up and ran for the door. As the Hebrews followed Moses, we ran after Dov. Mr.

Schwab would be instantly left alone, looking at his watch, which was never on time, with a puzzled look on his face.

We often played softball after school and called ourselves "The Oys of Summer." Playing other Hebrew schools, we put a lot of bagels on the scoreboard, and I, as usual, couldn't hit a bagel, even one stuffed with lox. One day after a game, Dov came up with one of his comic books he used to read in class.

"You want to see a dirty book?" he asked.

"What's that?" I asked.

"Yeah. It's about Popeye and Olive Oyl, and they're doin' it."

"It? What's *it*? Let me see."

"Keep your hands off. It's mine. I paid two dollars and it'll cost each of you a quarter to look," the smart-ass demanded.

"But that's all I get for allowance."

"C'mon, c'mon, hand over the money," Dov said.

With sexual thoughts pounding me into submission, I had no choice but to give him a quarter for relief. That was the first time I paid for sex. What else could I do? Fifteen years would pass before *Playboy* came out.

He took out the small comic book entitled, *Popeye Loves Olive Oyl*, and we all gazed at the creation of mankind.

On page one, Popeye was eating a can of spinach and flexing his muscles. On the next, Olive Oyl walked in, wearing an open gown, and Popeye had a bulge in his pants. On the following pages, the more spinach he ate, the bigger the bulge grew. I decided right then to eat more spinach. Popeye threw away the spinach and — started cooking with Olive Oyl.

Thanks to Dov, I finally understood the birds and the bees. Sex was no longer the forbidden fruit. I never did believe the baloney that I came from a fruit. Mama was wrong about cantaloupes — I had to eat more spinach.

How Rod and My Staff
Found Comfort

"To love oneself is the beginning of a lifelong romance."

— Oscar Wilde

Now that I had discovered the hot-rod between my legs, what was I supposed to do with it? The only Olive Oyl I could find was in the refrigerator along with the chicken-fat and Raskas Smetana sour cream. Meanwhile, erections, like a many-headed Hydra, were coming up all the time. I'd slap one and another would pop up. I took my fist and knocked it out, only to have it rise again, like a punch-drunk fighter.

I felt a flood surging in me, which I could not hold back much longer. I also noticed in the mirror a horn growing out of my forehead, above my right eye. I was, in other words, ruthlessly horny.

I was a precocious child; I masturbated early. What's so bad? At least you're making it with someone you really care about and you don't have to dress up.

I asked the rabbi if masturbation was okay and he sternly told me it was a sin according to the biblical story of Onan, who spilled his seed in the ground. He warned me that some people experience some visual deterioration or go blind. I found that hard to believe. If the Jewish population of the world was about fifteen million, then about seven and a half million males must wear thick glasses or walk with white canes.

I remember skimming through *Life* magazine. How I loved those pictures of floods, tornadoes, Joe Dimaggio, General Rommel, and Adolf Hitler. Suddenly, I saw the most exciting picture ever to appear in *Life* magazine: Rita Hayworth in an exquisite, diaphanous, white silky nightgown. She was leaning over with a sensuous, inviting smile, her beautiful bosoms drooping into the silk of her lingerie.

The power of raging sexuality was turning my hot rocks to stones, otherwise known as "lover's nuts." The dam was about to burst, and I felt like my alter ego from the sixties, Alexander Portnoy, who with unsavory bravado wrapped his *shlong* in a piece of liver. But I could never stoop so low. I grabbed a pillow, and ran into the usually hot bathroom where, on the same day that the Japanese were pounding Corregidor, Rommel was ravishing North Africa, and Hitler was penetrating Russia, I was exploding into a pillow, making chopped liver of Rita Hayworth. I heated up so much that my glasses got steamed. I couldn't see. No, no, God help me, forgive me. I don't want to go blind. My glasses came off and I could still see. Maybe this was not such a big sin, after all.

In adolescence, sex would sometimes rear its mysterious head, my *putz*, in such unlikely places as study hall. There I was studying Latin, *amo, amas, amat*, I love, you love, he loves, when my eye moved off the page onto the white silk blouse of a gorgeous girl sitting in the next row. She was a curvaceous, beautiful blond, with the cutest little smile. I had quickly moved from *amo* to my dream *shikseh*, my *amor*, my love.

At my cramped desk I felt a bulge in my pants, a stirring in my loins. What was I to do? When the bell rang signaling the end of class, I was so embarrassed that I kept looking down, saying to myself, "Go down you stupid *momzer*! (bastard). Girls would pass by, sneering at me. They had to be aware of my plight and were probably quite proud of having caused my suffering. My darling *shikseh* rose and simply smiled at me, worsening my condition.

I would get up slowly, knocking my puissant *putz* with my right hand, sometimes pounding it with my fist, but I couldn't keep it down. I slowly "crotched" up, pulling out my shirt as a cover-up. Out of sheer desperation, I clobbered the boner with my Latin book until I swooned. That was the last time I ever used my Latin.

Tell It to the Marines

My parents always considered a military career a desirable profession, especially during the Depression, when jobs were so scarce. Since Pop's parents couldn't afford to send him to college, he entered into one of the most honorable professions, the U.S. Marine Corps.

When World War II began, Pop and Mama prepared by dragging Aaron on Saturday mornings to watch the Jerome P. Goldman American Legion Marching Band, composed mainly of veterans' kids dressed in gold and blue uniforms.

"Look at their colorful uniforms. Wouldn't you like to be like them?" Mama said.

"Uh-uh," my brother muttered, at a loss for words for the first time in his life.

"Look how much fun they're having playing the marches. Wouldn't you like to do that?"

"I don't think so," he said.

"Why not?"

"I can't play an instrument."

"So maybe they'll make you the director," Mama said before giving up.

When it came to careers, I was totally left out. My parents apparently assumed I would simply drift into something. Mama once observed: "I don't care what my Roddy does. He can do anything he wants. If he wants to be a ditch-digger, let him be an archaeologist."

Aaron was the star of the family. He, like Elizabeth Taylor, got all the good genes in the family. He had curly, full, black hair; I had a strained mop look. He was tall and good looking and had a lot of girlfriends, even *shiksehs.* I was jealous because I couldn't even look a girl straight in the face, much less talk to one. But I didn't resent him, I looked up to him. Maybe I could be like him someday.

Paradoxically, he was the one who paid most attention to me. He took me to the Fox Theater every Saturday for the special matinee for a quarter. Then we went to Kotners Restaurant on the corner of Kingsbury and De Baliviere for another special: cube steak sandwich, French fries, and cole slaw for thirty-five cents.

When Aaron turned eighteen, he enlisted in the Marines and was shipped to the South Pacific. I never understood why anyone would ever enter a branch of service with the highest casualty rates. When he called, saying he was shipping overseas, Mama sobbed all night. His ship was heading for Iwo Jima, when fortunately the island fell and his convoy was diverted to Palau Island.

I looked forward to the letters Aaron would send from somewhere in the Pacific. He loved nicknames. My father was "Dude" and I was "Stinky."

UNITED STATES MARINE CORPS

South Pacific
July 8, '45

Dear Mom, Dude, Granny, and Stinky,

The beach party I told you about was a huge success and a good time was had by all. Beer, Coke, steak, and a beautiful ocean, not to mention having the day off; but one look at next week's training schedule and you would see that we will make up for it double and triple. It certainly was fun though, while it lasted. (And we only had to carry six to and from the trucks, who were just too drunk to make it under their own power.) Some of us couldn't help but think, as we chewed into our steak sandwiches, what the people back home wouldn't give for a bite of it.

Last Friday evening, I attended my first religious service, and, Mom, I did not know what I have been missing. A service, just like in the States, with pulpit and everything to go with it (It certainly was swell seeing all those Yiddish noses again.). . . .

I didn't mind being called Stinky — although it was certainly an unusual term of endearment.

My father had complete faith in the Marine Corps to see my brother through the war. My mother crowded out the war by never reading the front pages and went about her days looking forward to Sundays, *shnoring* at Lena's house. As for me, I cringed every time I read about a new beachhead. I came from a long line of Marines, but I could not follow them. I was not meant for beachheads, foxholes, freezing snow, or boiling temperatures. My parents felt I was not meant for anything, believing that I had an F-S *Shlepper* exemption. I had no choice but to follow the path of my fellow comrade-in-arms, Napoleon, who rose from *shlepper* to general in the army. Neither he nor I would settle on becoming a mere corporal, like my father and my brother. I vowed somehow, through some miracle, to become an officer in the United States Army. Tell that to the Marines.

Pop
Once a Marine, always a Marine
Note the sergeant stripes — He was busted to corporal following a
barracks-room brawl shortly after the picture was taken in 1923.

Corporal Aaron J. Fadem
U.S.M.C.
(Stinky's brother)

The Enchanted Forest

❧

"In the Chill, Still of the Night."

— *Rosalie* by Cole Porter

In the summer of 1943, I discovered my second coping mechanism — the beautiful music that calmed my anxieties. For the next three summers, I found a refuge from my painful thoughts in my first job as a paperboy selling the *St. Louis Globe Democrat* at the Municipal Opera in Forest Park. At that time, the "Muny" was the largest outdoor theatre in the country. Finding myself in the fantasy world of operettas and musicals was like being in an enchanted forest. Every evening I was serenaded by songs like "In The Still of the Night." Sitting there, I was a "Babe In Arms," "Girl Crazy," and I felt like "Anything Goes."

Before the season started, three other kids and I gathered at the corner of Delmar and De Baliviere, across from the old streetcar yards and the giant clock in front of Moll's Grocery Store with a neon sign "1848" marking the year the store opened, to apply for the newsboy jobs. The newspaper distributors hired us all and told us to choose a "junior boy" or the one in charge. We flipped pennies against the wall of the streetcar station; the one whose penny landed closest to the wall won the job. The others flipped first, and one penny landed one millimeter from the wall. How could I possibly get closer? I closed my eyes and prayed to God for a miracle. I launched my penny like a missile in the air, with a high parabolic arc. The coin was heading for the wall and without a mid-course correction it would surely collide and bounce away. If only Werner Von Braun were at the controls.

As if from heaven, a small white feather gently floated down, just in time to caress and cradle the penny during its descent toward the sidewalk. The coin twirled and came to rest, leaning against the wall. I had won the junior boy's job. Oh, God, could it be that you do look after little *shleppers*? Was it your feather? I picked it up and put it in my pocket.

I became a leader of the paper gang. *The Globe* paid me five dollars a week to get the papers to the park, bring back the unsold ones, and collect the money. I stationed myself in the center of the east ramp leading up to the theater gates, where I would yell, "Get your mornin' *Globe* here! Get your *Globe*!" I received nine-tenths of a cent for every three-cent paper I sold.

During the summer I shouted headlines: "Heavy Losses in Pacific!" The ticket-takers at the Muny Opera, feeling sorry for me, let me in free every night. Without a ticket, I roamed around the 11,000 seats (now 12,000) and discovered the grass at either side of the theater people sat for twenty-five cents. I spotted my deluxe seat, the grass behind my personal water fountain at the front of the section.

The Muny was founded in 1919 on a vast hillside in the middle of Forest Park. I would sell my newspapers halfway down the east ramp leading to the entrance. "ALLIES WIN BATTLE OF MIDWAY," I would yell out as the chronicler of World War II. I noticed that as the war news improved, my tips went up.

After the show, the other paperboys and I walked through the park after midnight, past the lagoon, the fountains, the field house, and finally, Jefferson Memorial (my former "Yesson Moiles"). As we marched along we sang with gusto all the music of the twenties and the thirties. We were like Rudolph Frimi's *The Three Muske-teers*, the hit show of 1924: "We are the Musketeers ... "

Alexander Dumas would have been proud of us, but not everyone agreed. "Hey, shut up, I'm trying to sleep," came a voice. We had awakened some people who actually slept in the park on extremely hot nights. Air-conditioning did not exist in those days. Years later we would never have marched through the park; wary of the crime, we would have dashed for our lives.

Another week I called out, "Allies pound Germany! Heavy air losses!" When the Allies were invading North Africa, I was dreaming I was in the French Foreign Legion in the show *The Desert Song* by Sigmund Romberg. He is long forgotten, but there was a time when people were humming and whistling his beautiful, romantic tunes. To this day I whistle "Blue heaven and you and..." Hearing such beautiful melodies, relieved anxieties.

As I walked to work each evening, I began a calming habit I would continue all my life — whistling. So many beautiful melodies kept popping into my mind. I noticed that whistling a happy tune eased my anxieties. I can remember passing people in the park, past Jefferson Memorial, the Field House, and the lakes, whistling my favorite Jerome Kern tune, "I hear music when I look at you ..."

My friends and I gleefully looked for mistakes at the Muny, and watching shows seven nights a week, we found them. In the second act of *The Cat and the Fiddle* by Jerome Kern, after listening to "The Night Was Made for Love," the phone rings on a table, and an actor picks it up and says, "Hello." With this cue, a voice starts a conversation. One night the phone prop was accidentally left off stage. When the phone rang, the actor turned to pick it up. He looked under the table, around the table, and in the drawer of a nearby desk. He stood there, hand on his head, pondering what to do next. The audience roared. In a flash of genius, he picked up an imaginary phone and said, "Hello." The audience applauded. The show did go on.

Then came that long-sought day:

"D-Day invasion!"

In 1944, Sigmund Romberg's *New Moon* was shining on the Muny stage and we heard: "Give me some men who are stout-hearted men…"

At the end of the '44 season, in answer to Sigmund Romberg's call, the ushers, who were turning eighteen, were saying goodbye to the peaceful refuge of the park. Those "stout hearted men" were heading for the dangers of war, whose headlines I would be shouting the next year.

Although I am jumping ahead in my timeline, the next year brought the end of the war.

"A-Bomb Exploded." Everyone was joyous. This momentous headline meant the war would soon be over and my brother, then in training for the invasion of Japan, would be coming home.

"Japan Sues For Peace."

Then, the biggest headline of all: **"WAR OVER!!"**

The lady at the refreshment stand offered me a free end-of-the-war hot dog. I will never forget the burnt smell of that hot dog, with reams of mustard streaming down the bun and onto my shirt. The mellow yellow blended well with the grass stain on the rear of my pants from my deluxe grass seat.

A well-dressed man came up, his face beaming, and pressed a half-dollar hard in my palm for a three-cent paper, the biggest tip in the history of newsboys. I was elated. My private war was over.

These were was the summers of my content. Through music I had found a window of happiness during the pain of my youth. I wondered where that feather came from that helped me become Junior Boy, while I sat on the moist grass in the chill, still, of the night, listening to the sweet sounds of the Enchanted Forest.

V FOR VICTORY

～⊙～

As the war wore on, my friends and I trudged to Hebrew School where we toiled like the ancient Hebrew slaves in Egypt. Only we had little hope for an exodus. Dov was our leader, but he was hardly a Moses. He tried everything he could think of to get kicked out of school, but this was no easy task, even for this Machiavellian talent. Dov had the audacity to plant a little stink bomb in the wastebasket under Mr. Schwab's desk. He knew the unsuspecting teacher would eventually flick an ash into the basket.

Mr. Schwab sometimes risked burning himself by letting the ashes of his cigarette build up until, little by little, they fell on his clothes. He had burnt spots on his suit coat, which he unfortunately couldn't afford to repair. Inevitably, the ashes would become two-thirds of the cigarette, and poor Meyer would rush to the wastebasket, lest he set himself on fire.

Finally, he threw the crumbling cigarette in the basket.

Vrooommm! The stink bomb exploded, filling the room with the most awful odor.

"Agh!" Meyer cried out. "I smell a rat!" He ran over to Dov's desk and screamed, "I know you did it, I know it. Who else could think of such a thing?"

Dov looked at me as if to say that I could have done it.

The *chutzpah* (nerve) to shift the blame.

But Meyer Schwab was shrewd; he pulled Dov up by the arm, put his other hand on Dov's mouth like a gag, and brought him up to the smoke-filled desk.

"You did this. Admit it. Only you could be so resourceful." He let go of the gag.

"What are you going to do about it?" Dov asked.

"You'd like me to throw you out, wouldn't you? That would make you happy, but it would make me more unhappy. I'd rather see you tortured in my class."

He let go, and Dov crumpled to the floor. The little twerp deserved to remain enslaved.

He tried again at Chanukah by lighting all the *yarmulkas* with the menorah candle. They all went up in flames. All Meyer could do was hit him with his ruler several times. Apparently, our poor teacher was losing patience with his nemesis. Meyer's hands began trembling, his eyes blazed fire, his demeanor grimaced with menace.

We all cringed in our seats. He grabbed Dov by the ankles, yanked him out of his seat, and held him upside down, hoping for more evidence of this sacrilege to drop out of his mouth. "You're expelled from school, banished! I never want to see you again, and if I have anything to say about it, you'll never be *Bar Mitzvahed.*"

Dov, swinging by his ankles, raised his face toward us with a winning smile, while he shot out a Winston Churchill *V* for victory with the index and middle fingers of both hands. He didn't mean V-E Day or V-J Day; it was simply V-H Day or Victory over Hebrew school.

BAR MITZVAH* TIME

∿

After a year off from Dov, Meyer Shwab calmly announced
through a puff of smoke that we had to prepare for our *Bar
Mitzvahs* and to bring our parents in to discuss the date. He
explained that on our thirteenth birthdays we would become
men in the eyes of the congregation and obligated to do mitvot,
the commandments of the *Torah*.

The next day our rejuvenated teacher wore a new sports
coat, the first one I could remember in five years. The coat was
so new and shiny that not one ash mark was even noticeable
yet. He stepped to the front of the class, ruler in hand, ready
to teach his class.

Then a cacophony of screaming and cursing was heard outside
the door. To our and Meyer Schwab's amazement, in burst a
shrieking, *zaftig*, lard-assed, pork-barreled *yiddishe* mama dragging her son by the ear, kicking and screaming — the wizard
of noise, Dov Klein.

His mother kept yelling, "You're going to be *Bar Mitzvahed*.
Now shut up or your father's going to give you a whipping!"

Meyer Schwab began to tremble, his face ashen like his cigarette.

"No, no, no, no way!"

---

* Literally the son of the commandment. The ceremony held in a synagogue or temple in which the thirteen-year-old Jewish boy assumes
the duties of a man. This celebration was not mentioned in the Bible
but, rather, commenced in the fourteenth century. And thus was born
the catering industry.

"What do you mean, 'no way'?" said Mrs. Klein.

"He can't even speak one word of Hebrew."

"Go on, Dov. Show him you can say a word."

Dov, who could imitate any call in the wild, was silent.

"You can do it. You know, Yiddish for *hello.*"

"I don't want to!" cried Dov.

"Sh …sh, " she whispered in his ear.

"Sh," he said.

"Sh." She secretly pinched his arm.

"Sh. Ah!" he screamed.

She whispered *L* in his ear and goosed him.

"Shahh-h-l-oh-" he exclaimed. "*Shalom!*"

Meyer Schwab stood his ground. "That boy will be *Bar Mitzvahed* over my dead body."

"It's your funeral, but if you don't do something about that burning cigarette, you're going to cremate yourself," Mrs. Klein said.

"No way, no way. *Nothing* could change my mind."

"I wouldn't be so sure of that," came a squeaky voice from the hallway. It was Mr. Klein, a dapper, aristocratic little milquetoast, a perfect mate for his domineering ball and chain.

He walked up to the forlorn teacher. "Are you aware that I am on the board for the synagogue?"

"*Oy Veh*, I hate politics!" Mr. Schwab said.

"I am also the biggest contributor to the synagogue, and I don't care if my boy can't speak a word of Hebrew. He can memorize the *Torah* portion. Everyone in our family has been *Bar Mitzvahed*, and by God my boy will be, too."

Meyer kept shaking his head in pain.

"Dov," Mr. Klein said, "there'll be no more shenanigans out of you. No more bird calls, no more trashy comic books. You should be more appreciative of what we've planned for you. You're being groomed to take over my business. It's there waiting for you.

First, you're gonna get *Bar Mitzvahaed*, and if you don't, you're going to get a big whoppin.'"

Then Dov spoke. "You can force me to go to Hebrew school, learn the *Haftorah* (a portion of the five books of Moses), and push me up the steps to the synagogue, but there ain't gonna be a *Bar Mitzvah!*"

How could he not want all those *Bar Mitzvah* gifts? All those watches, ties, hoards of checks, and government savings bonds. They were enough for a thirteen-year-old kid to feel rich.

How could anyone escape a *Bar Mitzvah?*

The Kleins left, and my turn came when Mama came to visit Meyer Schwab and asked about my *Bar Mitzvah*. She and I were shocked when Mr. Schwab told us, "No."

"No?" Mama said. "My Roddy is a good boy."

"Are you sure he's not — how shall I put it? Dimwitted, a little retarded?" he said.

"Ah! I've never been so insulted!" Mama said.

She's insulted. What about me? What was I, chopped liver?

"He does nothing but fall asleep in class. And when I call on him, he suddenly wakes up with a 'Who, me?' "

"He's just tired after grammar school."

Meyer had mistaken my preoccupation with repetitive thoughts for retardation.

"Repeat the *Shma*," Mama said to me.

"Shma, Isreal, Adonoy …"

"He speaks, he speaks!" Meyer Schwab said. "All right, all right, since Dov Klein has forced my hand, there will have to be a double *Bar Mitzvah* on June 15, 1945."

A date that would go down in infamy.

THE DOUBLE BAR MITZVAH

No one could figure what Dov was planning. Here he was sitting next to us in Hebrew school actually studying his Hebrew book. You don't suppose he would actually go through with the *Bar Mitzvah* to please his father?

The fateful June day arrived, and I was the first of the double *Bar Mitzvahs*.

Mama dressed me in my new *Bar Mitzvah* suit with wide lapels and the pants two sizes too long so I could grow into them. Her answer was to sew them into a hem so they did not hit the floor. And then in the future, Mama would let the hem down each year as I grew up.

The old Sheri Tellim Congregation was at Westminster and De Baliviere Avenues, overlooking the old streetcar yards.

As I traipsed up the creaky stairs of the synogogue, I heard the cling-clang of the ancient rectangular shaped street cars slowly plodding along on De Baliviere Avenue.

I looked around at the packed synagogue, the rabbi, my relatives, Dov, and his relatives, the ushers guarding the only exit stairs. If Dov was going to escape, he would never make it. And he certainly wasn't going to jump out of a second-story window. My father put the *Tallis*, or prayer shawl, on my shoulders, and I sat down between my parents. For the first time in my life, I felt their pride in me. I was ready to become a man.

The *Torah* was taken out and spread out on the pulpit. My heart was pounding, and my hands were shaking as I got up to sing the blessings over the *Torah*:

"*Barchu Et Adonai Ham Vorach.*" (Praise the Lord to whom our praise is due!)

The rabbi greeted me with the *Yad*, the pointer, in his hand, which he used to point to every word in the *Torah* that I sang. In Hebrew the letters move from right to left, the opposite of English. Everything went according to scripture, until a beautiful white feather floated down as if from heaven and landed on the yad. I recognized the same feather that had caressed the penny, helping me land the paperboy job. Was the yad trying to send me a message, just like the "rod" in Hebrew school?

The *yad* suddenly started to move in the opposite direction, as if spiritually inspired to move right, left, down, and then diagonally. The rabbi, mouth agape in shock, could only look on as the yad led his hand.

The pointer led by the feather was now writing — yada, yada, yada. Oh my God. I read, "Rudovey Fadum-*Shlepper.*"

There I was in the Bible Code, the alphabet of God. My soul, like all the souls of all the Jews who have ever lived, was present at the foot of Mount Sinai when Moses brought down the tablets.

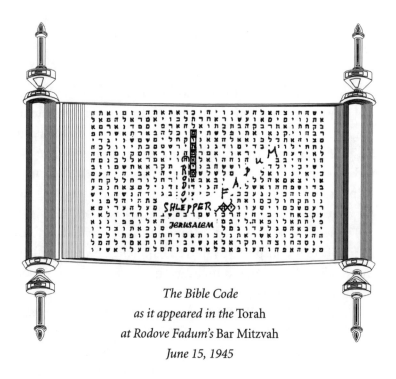

The Bible Code
as it appeared in the Torah
at Rodove Fadum's Bar Mitzvah
June 15, 1945

As I continued my Torah reading I felt a rising spirituality that touched my soul and my Jewish roots. I was fulfilling my Jewish heritage, when crack, like a bullet piercing my skull, a thought shot a holy terror into me: *Hate God, hate God, hate God.* No, no, no, not here. *Hate God, hate God.* I paused. I couldn't stop it.

"What's wrong?" the rabbi asked.

The thoughts continued pounding, pounding. I had to superimpose my hellish thoughts on every Hebrew word of the scripture. The conflicting phrases kept striking me. The tension mounted, the pressure rose like a geyser. I felt I was going to blow. *Hate God, hate God.* No, no, no. I could no longer hold back the pressure and spouted out with a roar, "Love God, love God, love God," throwing the yad up in the air.

The rabbi was shocked, the audience murmured.

The rabbi grabbed me. "What's the matter with you? Are you

meshuga?* Go on, you know the portion."

How could I, at the moment of my Jewish awakening, be so ashamed? At the moment of joy, I felt I was in hell.

I continued reading one phrase, and thinking another. I was shaking and the rabbi held my arm. I persevered and finished with one more, "Love God, love God."

As I walked back to sit with my parents the rabbi said, "I'm going to speak to your parents. I'm afraid something's going wrong in your head. You should be checked out."

I could only shiver in my seat and hold my head, hoping Dov would do something so outrageous that the congregation would forget me.

Dov stood up, and an air of expectation arose in the congregation. He ascended the pulpit and bowed slightly to the rabbi and the cantor. They bowed back respectively. Then one of the most bizarre events in the history of *Bar Mitzvahs* occurred. Dov spread his arms like wings and soared like a bird to the top of the pulpit. Then a flock of birds — macaws, parrots and cockatoos — began warbling in the far recesses of the sanctuary. The congregation looked around, taking their eyes off Dov and in that second, he screamed, "There ain't gonna be a *Bar Mitzvah*. I'm already a *Bar Mitzvah* boy," and disappeared in a puff of smoke. The mockingbird of the synagogue had flown away.

No one could believe it. Where'd he go? He couldn't have flown away. Or could he?

I was shlepping by the pulpit, when suddenly something cold grasped my ankles and pushed me down, down, sliding under the pulpit, where I found Dov's beaming face.

"Dov, what are you doing? Let go of my ankles!"

---

* Crazy.

"We sure did pull it off."

"What do you mean 'we'?"

"That was one hell of a *Bar Mitzvah* I never had! But I've got a secret to tell you."

"What's that?"

"The reason I didn't go through with the ceremony was that I found out I don't have to."

"You don't?"

"No. You neither. It's all just to please parents. You all looked down on me because I read comic books in class. But that's because I hated Hebrew school. Everybody does. But at home I like studying the Bible. According to Jewish law, the moment a boy reaches his thirteenth birthday, he is automatically *Bar Mitzvahed* and is obligated to do *mitzvot* [good deeds]. There was no way I was going to please my parents with a ceremony."

"You mean," I said, "after all this we're both *Bar Mitzvahed*?"

"That's the way the *kreplach* [dumpling] crumbles," he said, smilingly as he sneaked out of the synagogue.

The rabbi spoke to my parents afterwards but they didn't have a clue about me; they just thought I was shy and nervous.

At my reception at my house that afternoon, I received so many war bonds that there was little doubt that my Bar Mitzvah helped finance World War II. At the luncheon, the first of my now-famous mustard stains appeared on my beautiful blue tie, the result of a dripping kosher hot dog. On my left lapel materialized a large ketchup spot, obviously due to a faulty hamburger. And the biggest surprise of all was the glob of white mayonnaise on my crotch. How in the world could it have gotten there? I always kept my wonderful *Bar Mitzvah* suit in my closet, knowing that, in desperate times, I always had a meal waiting for me.

My bar mitzvah would prove to be a defining moment in my

life. Several momentous events swiftly followed. Two weeks later, my father irretrievably pushed us into the reformed Jewish age: he brought a ham into my mother's kosher kitchen. A month later the United States dropped the A-bomb on Japan.

THE SHLIPPERY SHLEPPER

The next day, Dov received one big whuppin'! I was now an adult in the eyes of the Sheri Tellim Congregation, but I was still a *shlepper* in the schoolyard. You may ask how I could be so sure I was born this way. I can imagine my DNA and the slide had a definite *S* curve. My chromosomes were marked *SH* and I have an *L* gene. Add it all up and shlep was written all over my body.

I would spend half my day waking up and then shlep myself along dragging my heels behind me, shlipping on telephone cords, rugs, and banana peels.

Would you like to become a *shlepper*? The closest thing in the gentile world would be a "nerd." The key is to be a disorganized mess. I never carry a briefcase — much too tidy. I prefer to put my papers in a shopping bag. I let them overflow to the point that a few of them fall on the floor or ground, just to let everyone know I've been there. In other words, I'm a bag man.

Stuff your pockets with tissue. Then when you need one, you'll always drop a few here and there so you can be sure to find your way back to your desk.

Always buy two ties with the same design. That way, you can have the opportunity to get various salad dressings on the number one. Number two tie is reserved for steak, chicken sauces and thick soups. Also, if you can manage to press a fork into Chicken Kiev, the butter has an excellent chance to hit your tie and glasses at the same time (a twofer).

After-dinner drinks also pose the great problem of how to escape being doused. The only solution for keeping your clothes and ties immaculate is to dine in a scuba suit.

After a while though, I grew tired of this shleppy behavior. Why did I feel so low, so anxious, so forlorn, so messy and disorganized? Is the mustard on my tie a symbol of what is wrong? Why am I always asking, *what if,* forcing anxious thoughts into my mind.

It would take decades before I would find the answer.

A. P. Cohen's Drugstore

After the *Bar Mitzvah* fiasco, Dov and I became friends and we hung out together. A. P. Cohen's Drugstore was a popular place for some of us after school. Dov was the first of my friends to get a job after school. He was the best soda jerk who was never *Bar Mitzvahed*. Even without a prayer, his fountain Coke was divine.

"You pour the Coke syrup," Dov would say, "just up to the line, two inches from the bottom of the glass, and then fill the rest with soda water. Mr. Cohen tells me if I go above the line with the syrup it ruins the taste." Then he added, "I would also lose money."

One day Dov rushed up as I was approaching the store and showed me something I had never seen before: a small cellophane-covered circular object.

"What is that?"

"It's a rubber."

"A what?"

"You know, some people call it a 'mancover' for your dick, so you don't make a baby during sex."

I had never seen anything like it before.

"You never know when you might need one of these," he boasted. "It makes you feel like a man."

That was how I would become a man? Dov, the pecker man, was going to show me the way.

"Come on in, I'll make a special cherry Coke, and it'll be on Mr. Cohen's tab."

This was a dangerous maneuver because Mr. Cohen was the

only proprietor I knew who charged mills (coins distributed to pay sales tax during World War II). You can imagine what he would do if he discovered Dov giving me a free Coke worth five cents.

"Look," he said, "in the first glass counter on the right of the first shelf."

"Cigarettes," I said.

"And you see next to them little covered packets."

"Rubbers?" I said loudly.

"Shh! You can't say 'rubber' out loud."

Mrs. Cohen was looking at me from the other side of the room. She was busy hiding some small boxes with a plain blue wrapper.

"What's she doing?" I asked.

"She's wrapping a box of Kotex," he whispered.

"What's Kotex?"

"Shh! You're not supposed to say that either."

"What can I say?"

"Nothing. Everyone thinks about sex, but you can't talk about it."

"I don't even know what Kotex is."

"I can't talk about it. It's so secret Mrs. Cohen is camouflaging them with the blue paper right now. All I can tell you is women need them once a month, and they don't want anyone to know they had the dreaded curse.

"You can't ask for anything directly. What you do is ask for cigarettes, which are okay. Then you shift your head and your eyes to the left, and Mr. Cohen will also shift his eyes a bit, reach down and bring out a new package of rubbers."

I observed some men come in. Dov told me guys would never go into their neighborhood drugstore, for they didn't want to be recognized. Some did want cigarettes, but, sure enough, I noticed them signal Mr. or Mrs. Cohen to sell them the camouflaged prophylactics. The women, however, would ask for breath mints and then move their eyes to the left. They got their Kotex.

"Go on, you can do it." Dov was definitely my mentor.

I walked up to Mr. Cohen, who was behind the counter, his bald head shining at me over his thick round glasses.

"You want something, sonny?"

"Uh, yeah, yeah. See those cigarettes? I'll have a Lucky Strike."

"Yes," he said, picking them up.

I moved my eyes to the left, but Mr. Cohen's look remained rigid. I looked over at Dov, and he was motioning with his hand, "Go, go on."

I kept shifting my head to the left.

"You got a nervous tic, sonny?"

"No, n-no. I-I want a-a — "

"A what? A what?" he said.

In the meantime, I was moving my eyes to the left, jerking my head the same way.

"What in the world do you want?" He raised his voice.

"I-I want a R-rubber and a Kotex," I yelled out.

What had I done? I had spoken the forbidden words.

Mrs. Cohen dropped her Kotex, her mouth wide open. Mr. Cohen dropped the cigarettes.

"I …I …ay-ay-yay-yi-yi," I screamed.

I rushed out the door, leaving Mr. and Mrs. Cohen as the defenders of good taste. Only years later would I carry a badge of manhood in my wallet, a gift from a kind soul.

ल

In 1950, I was marching at my high school graduation ceremony, heinous, vile thoughts struck me again.

Hate God, hate God, hate God. Stop, stop, stop, I inwardly wailed. The thoughts continued. *Hate God, hate God. Oh, God, stop it. Stop it.* I lowered my head. *"No-o-o-o-o-o-o."*

Repulsed, I felt I was committing a sin. Where did these thoughts originate? I knew I needed some help for something no one had ever heard of. I remembered the heavenly feather in my pocket and squeezed it, hoping for a miracle during next month's celebration of Chanukah. With the help of my third coping tool, fantasy, the miracle did happen.

Shlepper's Ladder

T'was the night before Chanukah,
And all through the house
Not a creature was stirring
Not even a spouse.
The children were nestled
All snug in their cradles
While dancing through their heads
Were visions of *latkes** and *dreidles*†.
T'was the night before Chanukah,
And Pop was *haking* Mama a *chainicka*‡,
And all through the night
While I was barely sleeping,
I kept hearing someone on the roof,
Noisily creeping.
I leapt from my bed, by Jiminy,
Just in time to hear this huge sound
Come crashing down the chimney.

— Clement Moore and I

---

* Potato pancakes.

† A small four-sided toy that children like to twirl at Chanukah.

‡ Haking a chainicka—literally banging a kettle, or talking a great deal.

I was aroused from a deep sleep, put on my socks, and rushed out of my room, slipped and fell, dropping some tissues and splitting my pajamas. Lifting my head, I glimpsed a figure crawling out of the fireplace. R-i-i-i-p came a loud noise. He looked ashen as he stumbled to his feet. He wore blue jeans, and two faded, white wings extended from his shoulders. While shlepping along, he would shed dirty feathers on the floor. Some of them landed close to my tissues. One close look, and I knew the feather in my pocket was the same as those on the floor.

I thought I must be dreaming for no one else heard a thing. "Who are you?"

"Who do you think I am? Santa Claus?"

"I don't believe in Santa Claus."

He limped over to the menorah and lit the candle with a brush of his wing. He held up a candle, illuminating his face. "Do you think I'm Chanukah Harry?"

"No, but who are you then?"

"My name is Shleppriel (pronounced shleppri-ale). I'm a *Malach* [angel]."

"The Jews have a long tradition of angels: Gavriel (pronounced gavri-ale), God's angel of destruction, who destroyed Sodom; Rafael, the angel of healing, who visited Abraham; Michael (miha-ale), the angel of faith, Uriel, the light of G-d, lighting the path in front of you. And, of course, there's Oreol, the angel of scrumptious cookies."

Standing there, he looked like someone I had seen in the movies or on television. He wasn't as suave as Cary Grant as Dudley in *The Bishop's Wife*, nor as old as Claude Raines in *Here Comes Mr. Jordan*. John Travolta and Nicolas Cage were just too gentile for my angel.

As Shleppriel continued talking, I noticed a comedic flavor in his spiel (talk.)

"What are you doing here?" I asked.

"Trying to find the world's biggest shlepper," he said. "That's why I've come all the way to Moscow."

"This isn't Moscow. This is St. Louis," I said.

"*Oy*," he said, slapping his forehead. "It isn't? Jeezus, I've always had a problem with directions. The Boss is pretty smart. I guess he figured the quickest way to come here was to send me to Russia."

"But you sent me those feathers."

"I was so busy flying around, lost, that I let them go and they found you. God works in mysterious ways."

I noticed some big red bruises on his forehead. "What are all those bumps on your head?" I asked.

"How would you look if you flew into fourteen telephone poles and six bridges?"

"Why have you gone through all this trouble to come to me?"

"Because my Boss said that after searching the world, you appear to be the perfect shlepper."

"How can you tell?"

"Tell?" he burst out laughing. "Just look at that rip in your pants. We call it '*Shlepper's* Rip.' Don't let it bother you; it comes with the territory. And your socks. One's blue and one's green."

"How do you know me so well?"

He lifted his right leg and showed a tear toward the rear of his pants. He raised his pants and displayed a brown sock on one foot, a yellow on the other. His shoes were untied. He gave me a mischievous glance and said, "It takes one to know one."

"You're one, too," I said.

"That's why they call me Shleppriel, (pronounced Shlepri-ale) the angel for shleppers."

"But why me?"

"God cares about all his people, from a king like David to the lowest *nudnick* [a nothing] like you."

"Am I worthy of being mentioned in the same breath with King David?"

"An angel may come to anyone who is deserving. You actually want to overcome your problems. You've embraced humor as one answer. As it says in Proverbs in the Bible, 'A merry heart doeth good like a medicine.' It certainly helps, but it is not the whole answer to your condition."

"What condition?

"You have a handicap."

"What is it?"

"I can't tell you."

"Why not?"

"The doctors don't have a name for it yet, but I promise you, you will learn more in time. Your obsessive thoughts are terrifying you now, but someday you will learn to deal with them. We are spiritual messengers from God."

"Yes, but what does that got to do with me?"

"Jacob fell asleep and had a dream about what many people now call a ladder, but what was really a staircase or ziggurat with angels ascending and descending on its way to heaven. Jacob didn't have to climb a ladder to get to heaven. Jacob's staircase promises God's blessing. It connects the angels of heaven to you on earth. When Jacob awoke he poured oil on the stone and called the place "Beth El" or "House of God.

"But this is your spiritual journey, " he snapped. "You have 'Shlepper's Ladder,' which you will actually climb. You may fall back, at times, but if you persevere, you will reach the top, *menshlekeit* [the attainment of *mensh*manship]. Your ladder may have *shlippery* rungs and you may *shlip* on an occasional banana peel, thus making you a *shlep-shlipper*."

I noticed a sign above each rung:

```
                              ┌─────────────────────┐
                              │      MENSCH          │
                    ┌─────────┤                      │
                    │    SHLEMIEL    │───────────────┘
          ┌─────────┤                │
          │   SHMENDRICK    │────────┘
┌─────────┤                 │
│    SHLEPPER    │──────────┘
│                │
└────────────────┘
```

"What does the ladder mean?"

"The first rung is how you feel now, a shlepper, or one who drags himself slowly through life in a messy, awkward style. Your repetitive thoughts and rituals are turning you into a disorganized slob.

The second rung is shmendrick, a born loser who is a shlemiel-in-training.

"You don't want to stay there, so your next step up will be to shlemiel, who is foolish, unlucky person, but who, by sheer luck, can come out on top."

"And then what?" I asked.

"You'll reach the highest rung, a mensh, a human being of the highest character. My feather will watch over you. It is God's will for you to improve. He will take you to the top."

"Will you be there, too?"

"Yes, but only to see you off."

He waved goodbye, and turned to fly out the window. Bammm! Unfortunately he forgot to open it.

"*Oy*, what I don't do for the *shleppers* of the world," he said.

The next day, I reflected on my nocturnal visitor. I couldn't have dreamed him up, but who would believe me? I had to believe in him. I was ready to commence on the voyage of my life. Different facets of my personality would soon emerge like my fictional heros: Don Quixote daydreaming his way though windmills; Walter Mitty going, "Topacata, topacata," and Leopold Bloom *shlepping* along the streets of Dublin on one day in James Joyce's *Ulysses*. If Bloom could represent the Odysseus of his day, then I could be the symbol of the wandering Jew, an Ill-Yid on his Oy-dyssey.

Thus ended the genesis of my life. I reflected on what my angel had told me about my handicap. Was it related to my increased need to ritualize and obsess over everything? I would'nt learn the answer for years. From time to time, however, thoughts of Hebrew school filtered through my mind, and of course, Meyer Schwab. By 1950, he had emigrated to the new state of Israel, and I had embarked on my exodus to the army. I wondered whether he would ever find his peace of mind or I my serenity.

How to Succeed
In the Army

Exodus

ↆ

By June 25, 1950, I had graduated from high school and my paperboy job at the Muny Opera and was preparing to enter Washington University. I was now an usher at the Muny Opera. Suddenly the usher next to me yelled out, "The North Koreans have invaded South Korea! It's on the radio," my fellow usher shouted. "Truman decided to defend the South and he's sending our troops!"

I continued showing people to their seats.

"The President just announced he's going to draft troops for Korea."

"What?" I awoke with a shout.

"That means us," were my friend's last words.

"Not me," I said. "I'm going to college, not war."

The Korean attack was my Pearl Harbor. I thought back to grammar school and my map of the Russian front with the arrow pointing to Stalingrad. But now the map on the front page of the *Post-Dispatch* showed a North Korean arrow streaking toward Pusan Harbor in South Korea, and pointing toward me. I could imagine the sign from World War II: Uncle Sam Wants You! Me! War was no place for a *shlepper*.

I had no idea what to study in college. I listened to every war report as I had done during World War II. Seoul fell and the outlook was bleak. I retreated to college. I didn't mind reading about war, but I certainly didn't want to fight in one. At least I had decided on my major: Staying out of Korea.

From Shlepper
to Shlemiel

~∂~

I enrolled in Washington University in the fall of 1950. While reading the university brochure, I noticed at the bottom of the page:

> Notice: For Up-and-Coming *Shlemiels*
> ROTC
> Reserve Officers Training Corps
> Graduate in four years as an officer in the
> U.S. Army Anti-Aircraft Artillery

That was it. I remembered my readings about Napoleon, who had joined the artillery and pushed his cannons to victory all over Europe.

Could I be like him? I found a biography that discussed his behavior in military cadet school. The French boys laughed at him, at everything about him, including his droll first name, Napoleon, which sounded like "*la paille-au-nez,*" straw in the nose, and that is what they called him for months thereafter."*

He sure sounded like me.

And then, about his basic training at the École Militaire, an early version of ROTC:

"Napoleon found daily drill in the large stone courtyard the most annoying and difficult of all the activities, with both

---

* *Napoleon Bonaparte* by Alan Schom.

sergeants and officers bellowing at him time and again for his slackness and unconcern, his mind forever elsewhere."

I could easily be like him. I felt a kinship with the "Little Corsecan," but I preferred to become a major *macher* (a big dealer.)

Early on Napoleon decided the surest way to advance in the army was the artillery, the power of the guns always led the way. It worked for him as he swiftly rose through the ranks. Naturally, I too joined the artillery. I also discovered in a rare French book that said Napoleon "était incapable d'utilisez un *fusil*";* he was incapable of using a rifle. So was I. We would be kindred souls in the military. I may be a *shlepper*, but boy did Napoleon ever shlep along on his way back from Moscow to Paris in 1812.

Mama couldn't believe the army would ever take me. Pop and Aaron, both corporals in the Marines, were shocked I would dare become a second lieutenant.

I was the first person ever to major in ROTC, and to minor in writing, literature, French, German, Russian, and all the other courses with which I would have great difficulty making a living.

The problem was the professors who didn't like my writing skills. I liked to insert humor in my papers on great literature. When I harpooned *Moby Dick* and called Ishmael a *shlemiel*, the professor blew his cork. He never had, in all his life, ever found a syllable of humor in academic writing.

My teacher also disliked my paper on Stendahl's *The Red and The Black*. I contended that the book was not about Julien Sorel's being torn between the black robes of the church and his longing for the power represented by the red coat of Napoleon. I argued, convincingly, that *The Red and The Black* was actually a "How To Play Roulette" guide.

I soon discovered some books were impossible to write about.

---

* "*C'est comme sa*," Jean-Paul Valei and Rebecca M. Valette, p. 28.

Freud's *Interpretations of Dreams* put me to sleep. But my fondest memory of my brand of rebellion was when I shocked the professor by stepping on the vermin in the bedroom of Kafka's *Metamorphosis*. Philosophy was a bore. To this day I kant read Kant. Though I loved Shakespeare, one professor criticized my using any form of the verb *to be*. So naturally I started my Hamlet paper with: "To exist or not to exist, that is the question." Clearly, Shakespeare couldn't save my writing career.

In addition to my professor's lack of humor, school proved no laughing matter either. Studying was difficult when repetitive thoughts were vying for my attention. Rereading sentences made finishing a book a long, laborious chore.

I always had feelings of anxiety and depression starting classes in September — in fact, beginning anything new. But the worst time of all was final exam week when, twice a year, I was living a nightmare: cramming all this knowledge of language, equations, and literature into my thick skull. My head felt like a squeezed sponge as I answered all the questions, going over and over the answers until I reluctantly was forced to turn in the blue test book. I slowly dragged myself home, groggy, and fell on my bed exhausted.

Soon enough, I began studying my major — ROTC: Military Leadership, Marching, Double-Timing, Artillery, Military Courtesy, Military Justice and Intelligence? What is there to do with someone who is totally unfit for the army? Make him 4F or, better yet, make him a second lieutenant.

I was not a round peg in a round hole but rather a square peg with nothing to fit into. I was right-handed and had an uncorrectable nearsighted right eye. I had to shoot left-handed. I couldn't hit a thing. I never saw a bull's-eye I couldn't miss. My voice was too high and too squeaky to yell out *Attention!* with any authority and I couldn't tell my right foot from a left shoulder arms. When faced with either going to Korea in 1950 as a private or joining

ROTC, the decision was easy. Why should I be a screwed-up private when I could be a fucked-up second lieutenant? I decided to become an officer and a gentleman.

When the unyielding force of army discipline collides with the disorganized mess of a born *shlepper,* it's enough to make the big bang seem like a cap gun. This collision occurred in the summer of 1952, when the ROTC sent me to summer camp in Fort Riley, Kansas. Because I had studied Russian in college, I applied for military intelligence and soon became a military intelligence-*shlepper*-cadet (a four-fold oxymoron). I always found the army moronic, it seemed so devoid of intelligence.

Fort Riley was not exactly an oasis but rather the most humid, polluted, wheat-filled air in the entire state. When I took my first deep breath and immediately began to wheeze, I realized I was allergic to wheat. My fellow cadets bestowed upon me a new appellation: The Wheezer.

I entered the whirlwind of the army. The supply sergeant threw oversized boots and undersized trousers at me and rushed me through a haircut and a series of shots. As a good soldier, I slowly walked over to the barracks with a pile of GI clutter: raincoat, canteen, steel helmet, dog tags hanging over my ears, and an entrenching tool sticking up over my head.

Everything about the army confused me. I didn't know what I was doing or where I was rushing to until I hit an immovable object — a tall, towering, muscular, ramrod of a soldier. All my army gear went flying high in the air, hitting one Sergeant Haman on the head with my entrenching tool. "What the hell!" he yelled, wiping some blood off the front of his head. "What's your name!" he demanded.

I responded with stunned silence.

"Don't you even know your name, you idiot?"

"Uh, uh, Fadem."

"I've never seen such a mess in the U.S. Army! Why the hell

did you drop all your gear on me!" Sergeant Haman hollered.

"I was daydreaming, Sergeant."

"You don't daydream in the army. You'll be blown away your first day in combat."

"Combat? I'm just here for training in military intelligence."

He looked at me sternly.

"Everyone is a soldier first and a specialist second. Now pick up all that junk and get ready for morning reveille. I'm going to take a special interest, you sad sack. When I'm through you'll wish you were in combat."

REVEILLE

$\mathcal{O}$

"O.C.O." — Oppressive, Compulsive Orders
or
"O.C.S." — Officers Candidate School

The first morning, the bugle sounded reveille at 0500 hours. The military saw 5 A.M. as the opportune time to mop the floor, clean the barracks, and make the bed with hospital corners. But I couldn't get up.

"Get up. Get up!" Someone was pushing me out of the bed.

"No, no, it's inhuman. I want to sleep. Please let me sleep. How can you get anyone up at five A.M. What an ungodly hour!"

The sergeant dragged me up and shoved a mop in my hand.

"Hurry up, soldier! How are you going to be an officer if you can't even get up in the morning?" the sergeant bellowed.

"Officers don't have to get up early in the morning," I said.

"You're not even a private yet," someone yelled.

I found myself in a row of moppers, and we all pushed forward. I felt like a zombie as I kept falling to my knees, the mop flopping in all directions.

I pulled myself up and finished mopping the *farshtunkener* floor at that miserable hour. The barracks were clean and ready for inspection and I had successfully fulfilled my first mission in the army. I had gotten up.

"Attention!" the first soldier yelled at the door as his highness, Sergeant Eugene Haman, tall, imperious and arrogant, marched in. He did not carry the scepter of his imperial descendant in Persia, who had persecuted the Jews several millennia ago. Instead he held a switch plucked from a tree, which he tapped against his other hand like the ruler which, no doubt, he had become.

He moved swiftly past the soldiers, each standing stiffly in front of his footlocker, waiting to be hounded for his imperfections. Haman stopped short in front of the quintessential punching bag destined to be pummeled into shape — me. "Raise your mop like a rifle. Place it on your right shoulder," he ordered.

He yelled — right face, left face, present arms, left shoulder arms, right shoulder arms. Left, right, right, left, over and over again. I was a ping-pong ball, a nonstop revolving door, a yo-yo. This was the beginning of everything, laid out for me from 0500 to 2400 hours. I found myself saluting more than I had ever checked locks and lights. If I broke a military regulation, I would feel guilt and fear or of winding up in the brig.

What was this obsession with giving orders in the army? What compulsion? O.C.O., Oppressive Compulsive Orders. I thought I was in Officer's Candidate School.

Did the army have the same problem I did?

Sergeant Haman called, "Halt." I spun to a stop and slumped over on my mop. *Now I'm ten, now I'm twenty. Now I'm twenty, twenty…*I had updated my ritual.

He glared. "What the hell is this?" he demanded.

"I'm a soldier, Sergeant."

"In what army?"

"Why…the United States Army."

"My army? You want to be in *my* army? Look at you! You've got your stinking shoes on the wrong feet!"

I winced. No wonder they hurt so much.

He leaned over, looking quizzically at my pants pockets, where he spied several thin white threads hanging down. I felt like telling him they were *tzisis*, a small *tallis* for praying that orthodox Jews wear, but he'd never get the joke.

He grabbed them, fingering them over and over again.

"What the hell are these?"

"Uh . . . floss."

"Floss? Used or fresh?"

"Uh . . . used."

"Damn it, damn it!" he yelled, shaking the floss off his fingers in disgust. He kept shaking, but the stuff stuck like glue. He finally wiped the floss off on my pants-leg as the other soldiers shot sideways glances at the spectacle I had become.

He looked at the rest of my outfit.

"What are those pants you've got on?"

"I think they're called fatigues."

"And that shirt?"

"I think it's called khaki."

"Then what is a khaki shirt doing with fatigue pants?"

"I just can't see straight early in the morning, sergeant."

"Get your hands out of your stinking pockets."

I complied with the order and pulled my hands out. Unfortunately, I was holding several tissues for blowing my nose in the allergic Ft. Riley air. They all fell to the floor.

"You dropped your shitty toilet paper on my floor."

"That's not toilet paper, sergeant. They're tissues."

"Clean it up!"

He began to remind me of Miss Hill, my first "sergeant" back in kindergarten.

I picked up my mess and promptly came to attention. I couldn't help my appearance. To this day I sometimes put on a blue suit coat with dark gray pants. Sometimes my socks are inside-out, and when I fix my tie the thinner inside end frequently winds up lower than the wider outside one.

The sergeant's eyes fell on the front of my pants.

"What the hell is that?" he said, pointing to my fly.

I looked down and saw, to my great embarrassment, my khaki shirt sticking out of my fly. Oy, I should not have rushed so much in the john.

The sergeant grabbed my shirt and pushed it back through, squashing my poor balls. I doubled over in pain. Remembering where I was, I slowly stood upright again.

"How can you be such a dumb ass?"

An answer came to mind but how could I tell him? *Now I'm twenty, twenty*....The pulsating, repetitive thoughts were tiring me. Thinking of two things at once wore me down, made me forgetful, absent-minded; neatness was evidently the last thing on my mind.

"Why don't you say something, slob?"

"I — I..." I looked down at my untied shoes and knew I had a problem.

"I'd like to run your sorry, sloppy ass out of the army. "But you ain't even *in* the army yet. I got to write a stinking report on you at the end of the summer, and I guarantee you, they won't be mistaking you for a Napoleon!"

What did he know about my hero? He was just as shleppy as me in his cadet school and look what happened to him.

The next morning in front of the barracks, Sergeant Haman stood proudly in the blue combat infantryman's badge above his left shirt pocket, his mustache sharply trimmed. All of him was perfect, except for the chaw of tobacco that bulged from his right cheek.

"I am Drill Sergeant Eugene Haman. I am here to teach you to be real soldiers, not textbook ROTC cadets. Think of me as God, and know that everything I say is The Law. I have absolute power over you. Cross me and you will feel my wrath," he said, sounding like a god.

"There's a war going on in Korea. I spent the last year there fighting while you soft college boys were playing soldier in ROTC.

You can forget everything you learned in college. It won't do you any good here. I've never stepped on a campus, but I'm sure it is nothing like marching through a minefield. I don't tolerate wimps and malingerers.

The sergeant began giving orders. "Attensh-hut! Right shoulder. Arms!" I thought of Napoleon's biography again:

As for the manual of arms, it was a positive bore, and week after week Napoleon was singled out for discipline. When the other cadets in his company were at "Present Arms," Napoleon would be at "Order Arms," and vice versa. "Civilize this dangerous islander," the drill instructor ordered....

My gun sling somehow got over my head and around my neck. "Ahhhhhh! Help! This carbine is strangling me!"

"I was in combat in Korea for two years. I've never lost a man to a rifle sling." The sergeant untangled me.

"Okay, men," he yelled. "Right shoulder arms! Fadem, why did you go left shoulder arms when I ordered right?"

"I guess I got mixed up."

"And what's the sling doing on your head again?" he said.

"I think I have a defective sling, Sergeant."

"What you've got is a defective mind!"

He was a Philistine who didn't understand. Although I was not the smartest soldier, this "dummy" was never going to set foot in combat. I would find a way to fight him back.

EN GARDE

At lunch in the mess hall the next day, the sergeant announced that the captain of our cadet corps had ordered us to assemble in front of our barracks at 1600 hours. At the assigned hour, we stood at attention when Captain Palmer drove up in his Jeep. He jumped out, and we saluted.

"Men," he began. "We have a very important, top-secret installation that must be defended at all costs. Do I have any volunteers?"

Silence. The captain walked up to the first line of cadets, looking at each man. He passed several, then stopped in front of me, staring directly into my eyes. "You look like an up-and-comer, soldier."

"Who, me? Ye-ss, sir."

He looked at the nametag on my shirt. "Cadet Fadem, do you want to succeed in this army?"

"Yes, sir."

"Are you up for a vital mission?" inquired the captain.

I held my head high and shouted, "Cadet Fadem, ready and able, sir!"

"Good, you've just volunteered to guard the Fort Riley tank for the night." My heart swelled with pride. Little me, guarding a giant tank, just like the ones General Patton had used.

"What kind of tank am I responsible for? Is it used in Korea?"

"Of course it's used in Korea. Our sewage disposal tank is the most modern technology. Our expert engineers have devised a continuous flow of waste material decomposed by anaerobic bacteria."

Oh, my God, why do I get all the crappy jobs?

"The whole chain of command places a high priority on troop hygiene," the captain continued. "That is why our latrines are kept spotless. You know what happens if this tank blows? We'll be shit out of luck. The general will come down on the lieutenant colonel, who will come down on me, and I'll bury you."

"*Oy vey.*" I grew nervous. "But, sir — "

"No buts. Get your ass in the jeep and I'll drive you to your post."

I noticed the large septic tank sunk into the ground with barbed wire surrounding the perimeter as I jumped out of the jeep and stood at attention at right shoulder arms.

"Oh, by the way," the captain said casually. "I forgot to mention something, not that it would pertain to you. There's a regulation that falling asleep on guard duty is punishable by death in war time."

"I-I … *oy*, what have I got myself into?"

"What's that, Fadem?"

"I said, boy am I ready to do my duty!"

"Good luck," he said as he drove off into the dusk.

I walked in a big circle, over and over again. The boredom of the duty was overwhelming, as was the increasingly heavy M-1 rifle pressing on my shoulder. Anxiety accompanied my increasing nervousness. My heart jumped every time I heard a foreign sound. I kept looking back every few minutes like I did on my way from school. I had to make sure no one was sneaking up on me. I kept circling for over five hours and did not find one spy, or saboteur, not even a cricket.

Crack!

What's that noise?

Snap!

Something was moving. The more anxious I became, the more my brain repeated thoughts. *I must stop the enemy, I must stop the enemy.* Again, in some magical way, I felt the thoughts would protect me. Another crack startled my ears. The enemy was moving toward me, now it was rushing me. My blood pressure soared and my heart pounded. I brought my rifle forward to the ready and yelled, "Halt! Who goes there?"

Silence.

A brushing noise, followed by a dark, blurry form, dashed straight at me. The foe was closing fast! I aimed my rifle, my finger twitched on the trigger, when suddenly I saw my intruder — a big, black rodent. I smashed at his head with the stock of my rifle. He went limp and I thought I had scored a knock-out punch, but he raised his head, then his body, and slowly *shlepped* again toward the tank.

"Get away from the tank. Do you want to get me in trouble?" I flipped him away with my rifle.

I was astonished at what had taken place. How could I volunteer to guard a *farshtunkener* septic tank? How could my first experience in combat turn out to be a rodent? Because I was born a *shlepper*, that's how. I had met the enemy and he was me.

Having stopped the encroaching enemy, I felt I deserved a little rest. I slumped down to the ground and leaned against a nearby tree. I was bushed. What harm could there be in taking a little nap? It was 0300 hours. The captain wasn't going to get up just to check on me. I felt so drowsy, so sleepy. Why couldn't —

I was back in high school. The beautiful blonde *shikseh*, whom I could never approach, was standing over my desk asking if she could help me up. But I didn't dare rise because of my erection. Her beautiful lips came toward me until she kissed me and sent me into my seventh heaven.

"Ouch! Aghhh!" I screamed. "I'm shot! I'm shot! Aghhh! My ankle! My ankle!"

I woke to find the damned rodent gnawing at my leg. "What are you doing? You little twerp!" I hit him again with the butt of my rifle. He backed off for a moment, then scrambled back and grabbed my torn pantleg.

"Let go, let go!" I said as I raised my rifle at the little pip-squeak.

Then I heard a noise in the distance, the rumbling sound of a Jeep. Oh, my God! The captain was coming to check on me, and the poor rodent was saving my ass from a court-martial.

I quickly stuffed my shirt in, put my cap back on, brushed the dirt off my rear, and was ready to salute Captain Palmer as he jumped from his Jeep.

"How did things go, Fadem?"

"Very good, sir." I had stopped the enemy.

"Why is your pant leg torn?"

"A rodent tried to sneak in, but I fought him off." The wound was now bleeding.

"Fadem, I'm impressed with your dedication. You've done such a good job, I'm volunteering you again for tonight's guard duty. I can sleep now knowing the tank is in secure hands. Better get yourself over to the infirmary and get a rabies shot!" He saluted as he drove off.

I sat down and my persistent rodent friend reappeared.

"Come over here."

He sneered at me.

"Can't we be friends? We have a lot in common. Ever since grammar school I've been called Rodent. I imagine you've been called rodent a lot yourself."

He turned up his nose.

"You're not mad over me hitting you, are you? I didn't mean it. You saved my butt. I was only doing my duty. I hope you understand. Will you forgive me?"

He scrunched his nose as he turned away. Then he looked back, raised his hind paw, and gave me a squirt. He scampered away pissing me *au revoir*.

THE DOUBLE TIMER

The wheaty air at Fort Riley forced itself into my bronchioles, forcing me to wheeze almost all the time.

"March, two, three, four! March, two, three, four! Cadet Rodent! What in the hell are you doing?"

"I'm marching, Sergeant."

"That's not marching, that's shuffling!" he shouted.

"No," I said, "that's *shlepping.*"

"Well, you're sure as hell going to move it around here, or you'll be out of here!"

I *shlepped* up the pace. "Sergeant, sergeant, I'm having trouble breathing!" I wheezed out at him.

"Quiet in the ranks!"

"I - huh-h-h-h. I'm allergic, Sergeant."

"To what?" he asked.

"To Fort Riley."

The warm and humid air made me wheeze faster than I could waddle along.

The sergeant ran up to me. "What the hell are you? A bastard malingerer?"

"I can't b-b-breathe, Sergeant."

"I don't want goddam excuses. Pick up the pace."

Oh, to find somewhere I could hide, while away the hours, and creep back to my bunk. But not even a shrub was to be seen in the distance. Oh, God, couldn't you get me a bush? It doesn't have to be a burning one.

Then a miracle occurred. In the distance down the road, through the haze, was a mirage. A temple with four columns across the front with Jewish stars on top of each. I yearned for such a sanctuary.

"You're getting behind, Fadem!"

"I can't keep up, Sergeant. Can't you slow down?"

"Double-time, march!"

The sergeant kicked up a pile of dust, which made me sneeze and wheeze. I slowed down and let the others pass me by. I staggered toward the temple, which suddenly disappeared. In its place was a deserted gas station with four ancient gas pumps. On top of each was a Texaco star. As I entered the old building my feet went through the top of the rotted floor. I caught the top of the counter and hoisted myself up to its top.

I lay down on the old counter and looked at the shabby walls. I had found my sanctuary. After a nap, I sauntered back to the peace of the barracks and the coziness of my bunk. I dropped my dirty rifle, canteen, and shoes on the floor.

"Where the hell have you been? You rodent!" the sergeant barged in and yelled in my ears. "You snuck out of formation, I know you did!"

"No, I made it all the way back!"

"I don't believe you. Look at you, a stinking mess. You're a piss-awful disgrace to the army. Someday I'm gonna get you!" He walked away, leaving me fearful of our next encounter.

The next afternoon, we learned about the rifle. We assembled in the barracks, and the sergeant held up the weapon.

"This is an M1 gas-fired carbine rifle. It can fire a ten-round cartridge automatically and kill an enemy at a thousand yards, or your foot if you're a careless asshole." The sergeant paused for effect. "Now, remember, this is a rifle, not a gun. This here rifle goes *pop*, hitting a north Korean, the gun goes *brrrrm* at a MIG jet. We're very particular in the army with our weapons. Gangsters use guns, we fire rifles.

"Your goal with this weapon is simple: kill the enemy." He

pulled a bayonet from its sheaf and attached it to the rifle barrel. "If you can't shoot the bastard then it's your duty to carve him up like a turkey with a carving knife." I could accept the idea of an enemy doing away with me, but I recoiled at the image of a knife like the one mama had held when she offered me a piece of chocolate cake.

Pick up the knife and stab someone.

Pick up the knife and stab someone.

The only way to turn away the pain of anxiety was to day-dream. I was back as an usher at the Muny Opera hearing my favorite calming music. "Why do I love you?" "The night was made for love." "Blue heavens and — "

"RODENT!" A scream brought me back to the barracks.

The sergeant startled me.

"If you fall asleep on guard duty in combat with this weapon," the sergeant warned, "I could have you shot."

"Yes, Sergeant," I said, knowing full well that the knife still haunted me.

The sergeant continued: "Now the first thing you have to do is take the carbine apart and clean it. Now lower the trigger latch and take it apart."

As everyone started to strip down his rifle, fistfuls of small metal parts hit the floor by my feet.

"What was that?" Haman was intent.

"Uh, uh, I spilled my rifle parts. I couldn't help it. The parts blew right out of my hands." I looked at the parts, some big, some small, but my mind refused to focus on them. *Pick up the knife and stab someone* blocked them out.

"Pick them up. Pick them up, you cretin! You're not smart enough to be in military intelligence. "Now everyone assemble your rifles!"

"Sergeant, I've got to be honest with you. I'm not mechanical. I can't put the rifle together."

"What did you say?"

"I'm sorry."

"You dummy!" he said. "Every officer since the Revolution has managed to assemble his weapons. What the hell are you going to do if your rifle gets dirty in combat?"

"Why should I have to worry about cleaning a rifle when I studied 90mm guns at Washington U.?"

"But you have to put that rifle together or you'll never pass this training."

I tried and tried, but my mind could not concentrate on the stinking parts. Like Humpty-Dumpty, I couldn't put my rifle back together again. The barrel of the M1 wouldn't fit into the trigger housing Nothing worked. So I jammed all the parts together. When I was through, it looked like I had reinvented the carbine.

I put the contraption to my shoulder and peered through the aiming sight. There, staring me in the face was the barrel of the rifle. If I pulled the trigger, I would have blown my head off. But at least it was together. Maybe I could still become an officer.

When the sergeant announced we were going on the firing range the next day, I gasped. The whole platoon could be shot up if I used that weapon. I thought my fellow soldiers would be eager to help me, but they just looked away. I finally had to bribe one of them ten dollars to resurrect the damn rifle.

SERGEANT YORK

Of all the movies of my childhood, Gary Cooper in *Sergeant York* left the most lasting impression on me. I saw the movie twelve times and knew the lines. How I longed to be brave enough to capture 128 Germans single-handedly and kill dozens of others. I decided to switch from Napoleon, who couldn't shoot straight, to Sergeant York, the greatest marksman of World War I.

He was my hero: brave, resilient, strong, and a marksman. Only one major difference stood between us: I couldn't shoot. Thus, I felt both elation and trepidation when the sergeant announced we were marching to the rifle range to qualify with our M1 carbines. As I marched along, Gary Cooper's chiseled features swam in front of my eyes. If I tried, I knew I could be him. I thrust my shoulders back, held out my chest, and stepped up the pace while I transformed myself into the brave sergeant. No longer was I wearing the green fatigues of a cadet but the 1917 khaki uniform of a World War I doughboy.

My cap changed into a wide-rimmed brown doughboy hat. I looked down and saw the distinctive Sam Browne belt, which diagonally crossed my chest and attached to my regular belt.

As I arrived at my assigned position on the firing range, I noticed my pants were turning into the World War I vintage Indian jodhpur breeches or leggings. It's what Sergeant York would have called them. I assumed the prone firing position.

Sergeant Haman came over to me. He paused a second, probably contemplating my new look.

"OK, Rodent, let's see what you can do."

I licked my thumb and marked my sight with some saliva,

Alvin York style.

"What are you doing there?" the sergeant asked.

"I always wet my sights, Sergeant," I said in a great imitation of Gary Cooper. "I always do that when I set out to do some serious shooting. It cuts down on the haze." I remembered the exact words from the movie, because I had watched it so often.

"Now set your sling on your arms and make sure the front sight divides the rear."

The announcement came from the loudspeaker:

"Ready on the right,

Ready on the left,

Ready on the firing line.

Ready — Aim — Fire!"

I closed my left eye and aimed the sight at the target. I squinted my amblyopic right eye, but all I saw was fog. They say you can't see what you're shooting at in combat, so I felt quite at home. I pulled the trigger and shots resounded in every direction. What if I miss? What if I miss? How will I ever become an officer?

"Cease fire!"

We waited for the soldiers in the target pits to put up a round marker indicating a bull's-eye or a two, three, four spot off center. Instead, they raised a red flag. Someone yelled, "Maggie drawers." That was an old army term for missing the target completely.

"Miss!" the sergeant yelled. "You can't even hit the target. What do you see when you look through your wet sight?"

"Nothing, I have a bad right eye. It's like looking through a fog."

"How dumb can you be? You're more dangerous than the enemy. Shoot left-handed." I switched but found I could not hold the rifle left-handed. I pulled the trigger with nervous fingers.

"Maggie drawers. Missed," came the call.

Just like Sergeant York, I protested. "I don't reckon how I could miss that there target, Sergeant," I said.

"Mark the target again," he shouted. The target was marked and I shot again.

"Maggie drawers."

"I can't understand how I could miss that whole thing. I followed everything Sergeant York did in the movie about him."

"York! That's it. You think you're Sergeant York. What kind of dreamer are you? In World War II, you'd say you were Audie Murphy. I've known a lot of soldiers, but Rodent, you're no Sergeant York!"

Immediately, my wide-brimmed hat, Sam Browne belt and jodphur breeches disappeared. I was just another *shlepper* in fatigues. Everyone was required by the army to qualify once a year on the rifle range. But without some supernatural aid, I could never pass.

"Listen, Rodent, how do you expect to be a leader of men in combat when you can't even hit a target, much less a bull's eye? I'm not going to let you be an officer who can't shoot. It's never happened in the history of the army. You have one chance, or you're out. Here's your last bullet. Hit the bull's eye or you'll wind up in Korea."

I gulped. A foxhole in Korea was no place for a *shlepper*. I'd never come back. I placed the bullet in the chamber. My hands shook. How do I hit the target with nervous fingers? Calm down, calm down. Use your reasoning. When you aim at the bull's eye, where does the shell go? Not even on the target. Therefore, if I aim off the target and in the air, I stand a far better chance of hitting the bull's eye. Ergo, don't shoot like Sergeant York, shoot like Napoleon. Oh, Shleppriel, please hear my prayers. I need a real miracle this time.

I pressed the trigger, and *pow*, I fired the shot heard round the universe. A white marker went up. Bull's eye.

"What?" I yelled. For the first time in my life I felt like a butter-fingered *shlemiel* who somehow manages to land on top.

"What? I can't believe it," screamed the sergeant. He grabbed his binoculars and looked in awe. "I'll be damned! There's the signal. They're waving a round white marker," he said, putting down the binoculars. "What d'ya know. We've got a Sergeant York among us."

I had still "bollowed" or failed the marksmanship test, but the sergeant kept his word and let me proceed with my training. Had I discovered a new way to be a sharpshooter? Only the soldiers in charge of cleaning up the used targets knew that answer.

"Look at this," one said. "There's a little feather's stuck on the bull's-eye. Heaven knows where that came from."

I was comforted by the thought that my hero, Napoleon, was my *shlepper*-in-arms, couldn't shoot, either. And look how far he went.

DAVID AND GOLIATH

At 0600 hours the next morning, I was busily doing my mopping chores. I wondered why every minute, every hour, was planned in the army. In a way, it was like my civilian life, my needing to do things the same way every day. I was beginning to feel more at home.

"Atten-hut!" said the sergeant.

At the Saturday morning inspection, I stood rigid in front of my bunk, holding the rifle in front of me with the bolt open. Sargent Haman no longer looked like the malevolent King of Persia; rather, he was Goliath, the nine-and-a-half-foot tall giant Philistine with "his brass helmet and coat of mail weighing five shekels."

The sergeant grabbed the weapon and looked down the barrel.

"There are two specks of dust at the bottom of this barrel. By sixteen hundred hours, you will have this rifle absolutely clean, and you will take it and seven other rifles to bed with you."

Then he looked at my bed and stuck his hand between the folded sheets. "What's this?" he said as he pulled out a long brown sock.

"It's a sock, Sergeant."

"I know that, but what's it doing in your hospital-corners sheet?"

"I seem to lose things, Sergeant."

He took a quarter out of his pocket and flipped it on the bed. It landed flat like a lead weight. "It's supposed to bounce. Add two more rifles to your bed tonight."

The inspection was over and I, like King David, pondered how I would defeat my nemeses. He with a javelin, a sword or a spear; me with no armor, only my unloaded rifle with some dust spots on its bore. I could find no sticks or slings or stones, so I had to create my "Goliath-equivalency" weapon.

I rushed to the PX and bought some Tide detergent and a turnbuckle that could tighten the springs of a mattress so that when released, it would explode.

Back at the barracks, I grabbed my rifle, stuffed it with Tide, and stood it straight up in the shower. I turned the water on, and let a torrent of suds wash it for two hours. Then I rinsed out the soap and let the shower run another hour before letting the rifle dry.

In the meantime, I turned the mattress over and duct-taped both sides of the bedspread as they came together under the bed. I then attached the turnbuckle to the springs so tautly that it became my slingshot. I flipped the mattress back, mentally substituting a quarter for a stone. I was sure it would soar like a missile. Over and over I thought, *I have to get even with him, have to get even, get even.*

The sergeant arrived as promised. He seized the rifle, looked at the open bolt, clean as a whisker. He turned it up, down, crosswise, and exclaimed, "I'll be damned! That's the cleanest rifle I've ever seen in the entire army. But that smell is so odd. I can't quite place it. Why would a barracks smell like a laundromat?"

He handed the rifle back to me. I prayed that he would not snoop around the bed. The quarter, just flip the quarter. Forget about my damned socks, I thought.

He looked around, bent down at the rigid hospital corners of the bed. *Don't touch the bed,* I said to myself. He stood up and said, "This is amazing. It's the tightest bed I've ever seen. I can't believe this. You could eat off this floor, too. You sure you didn't bribe someone to do this?"

"No, Sergeant. But what about the bed?"

"What about it?"

"Aren't you going to check how taut I made the bed?"

Flip the coin, flip the coin, flip that damn coin, I kept saying to myself.

"I don't have a quarter. Somehow you've managed a miracle. Forget about the rifles."

"Here, take my quarter," I said.

Unlike David who carried five stones to the battle, I had my slingshot made of springs, preparing to fight Goliath. And the smart money was betting on Goliath.

Finally, he grabbed the coin out of my hand and slammed it onto the bed.

The noise of springs erupted and the quarter shot up like a missile, hit the sergeant in his right eye on its way to the ceiling, then hit the window. After bouncing a few more times, it finally landed flat on the bed.

"My eye! My eye! I can't see! What happened? Are we under attack? Who's shooting? Are the North Koreans attacking Fort Riley? Call the alarm!" The sergeant kept shouting, while crawling for cover on the floor, finally hiding under the bedsprings, his arms covering his head. "Get down, get down! Get all the rifles to the men! Sound the alarm! I can't see!"

"Don't worry, Sergeant. You can be like me now. Shoot left-handed!" I was ecstatic, vindicated.

"No, no. That's the worst thing I can imagine. What am I doing hiding under the bed?" he asked. "You shot me with a quarter?"

"How could I? You know I can't shoot," I said.

"You shot me with a quarter?"

"No way, Sergeant."

"Then who did it?"

"The bed," I said.

"The what?"

"The bed. The springs malfunctioned, just like a slingshot. And you thought I couldn't shoot straight."

He put his hand to his swollen black and blue eye, glared at me with his good eye, and staggered to the door.

"You wouldn't tell anyone, would you?"

"They'll believe me. Only a *shlepper* like me could have thought up something like that. On the other hand, if I say I came to present arms with my rifle held straight out when you commanded 'Attention' and inadvertently slammed your right eye, they'd believe that, too, because they all think I'm a *shmuck*."

"You'll say that?" There was a glimmer of hope in his eye.

"Sure. For a passing grade for summer training."

"What!"

"I'm not asking much. I just want to stay in school."

He paused and said, "Yeah, I get it. Okay. I wouldn't want you in Korea, anyway. Especially around me. You'd shoot me. And we might lose the war."

He swaggered out of the barracks, and I sighed with relief. I'd done it. I was going to get through this miserable six weeks at Fort Riley and return to Washington University. I leaned back on the bed with relief. I thought of my victory over Goliath. As the Bible says: "How the mighty has fallen." But it also says, "Pride goeth before a fall." I didn't fully grasp what that meant until …

"WHMMMP!"

I fell through with the springs, duct tape, nuts, and bolts, collapsing to the floor. I roared with laughter, savoring the sweetness of my revenge.

For the last two weeks of training, the sergeant wore dark sunglasses. When we assembled before the barracks for a final ceremony, the sergeant took off his sunglasses, revealing a shiner as big as cyclop's eye. "You have completed your summer training. A few of you may become excellent officers, and some of you will be lucky to become a Sergeant York. If you don't make it, there's nothing wrong with becoming an enlisted man. We fight the wars. Officers just give orders. I want you to know I have re-upped for Korea. After my vacation with you college boys, it will be a pleasure. Anyone wish to join me?"

No one moved. Standing at attention was far preferable to Korea.

"I can't tell you how relieved I am," the sergeant said. "I have no intention of being a casualty. Squad dismissed."

Thank heaven! Summer camp was over. I got my army gear together — helmet, fatigues, boots, dog tags, and the entrenching tool sticking up again above my head. I ran around the corner of my barracks and straight into the poor bruised sergeant. The entrenching tool hit his good left eye, and everything went flying.

"No! No! Not again!"

Two black eyes were the sign of a heroic combat infantryman. He could always say an artillery shell went off near him.

"You again!"

"I'm so sorry, Sergeant. Let me help you up."

"No, no, don't touch me. Don't come near me ever again. I'm safer in combat!

I returned to Washington University and I marched down to the ROTC quonset huts, where I was greeted by one of the best officers I had ever met, Captain Dahlquist. He wore horn-rimmed glasses, smoked a pipe, and looked sharp in his Eisenhower jacket.

He was an expert in anti-aircraft artillery, but what made

him special was that he frequently smiled kindly at me. Smiles appropriate to the army range from sardonic, tense, fearful, to gruesome. But kindness was not a touchstone for success. That could be a fatal flaw. Despite this, Captain Dahlquist was an amazing officer whom I greatly admired. Besides, he liked me.

He called me into his office and showed me my evaluation report. "It says here you 'passed — with reservations.' "

"Reservations?" I asked.

"Yes." He turned the page a moment. "This . . . ah . . . Sergeant Haman says here you can march, but you can't double-time. You can shoot, but can't qualify. You mean you didn't qualify with the rifle? That's really not good, Fadem." He continued: " 'He can take a rifle apart, but he can't put it together again. When he shouts orders, he wheezes. He seems to be allergic to the army. Other than these reservations, he could make a very fine officer.' This is without doubt the strangest performance evaluation I have ever seen," the captain said. "Wouldn't you agree, Fadem?

"And look, there's a footnote. The sergeant sent you a special commendation for defending a septic tank against a marauding rodent. This changes the picture. You do have some potential."

"If you give me a chance, I know I can do well, sir," I said.

"Okay, Fadem, we'll give you another chance. The army needs officers right now."

Either Captain Dahlquist was an astute officer, or the army needed expendable second lieutenants in Korea much more than I dreamed.

Back at school, in ROTC I had to make all *A*'s to cover up my failings on the field. Everyone else didn't give a hoot about ROTC; I could easily outshine them all treating the subject as my major. I received a 97 in map reading even though I would probably get lost in combat. But the Korean War was not over as

General MacArthur had predicted. We all thought we were winning until to ours (and MacArthur's) great surprise the Chinese came in. Would my prediction be wrong too, of the war ending in four years? The news of peace talks in Pyongyang was music to my ears. By 1953, I was third in the class academically and about five hundred and fourteen militarily. I had squeaked by, like Job, by the "skin of my teeth."

One fine day in June, a large brown envelope arrived in the mail with U.S. Army markings on it.

FROM: Headquarters Fourth Army
          Fort Bliss, Texas

TO: Roodoowe Wesley Fadem, II
          St. Louis, Missouri

The Secretary of the Army has directed that you be informed that by direction of the President, you are appointed a Reserve Commissioned Officer of the United States Army and are hereby proclaimed an Officer and a Gentleman.

May I add my sincere congratulations.

By Order of:
Dwight David Eisenhower
President of the United States

P.S. Please forgive me for not being able to pronounce or spell your name. You are to be saluted for being the first officer in the army since 1776 who could not qualify with the rifle.

Mama Joins
The Army

The next week I and the other ROTC cadets all stood in the hot sun outside the Quonset hut at the west side of the university, awaiting our gold bars. When Captain Dalquist pinned the gold bars on my collar, I again felt pride in myself. I, like that *shleppy* little Napoleon cadet, had risen from obscurity to an officer and even a gentleman. This had to be a miracle from my guardian angel. My father and brother left the Marine Corps with the rank of corporal, but I, little Stinky, had risen, like Lazarus from the grave, to the rank of lieutenant.

Mama and Pop and the other families eagerly watched. According to tradition, the sergeant who gave us our first salute received a ten-dollar bill from the newly minted lieutenant But there was one problem; I only had a five.

I enlisted Mama's help in procuring one and she strolled away to find the money, even though the sergeant said he was happy with just the five. But the thought had found a home in my mind. *Ten dollars, ten dollars, ten dollars.* Round and round it went, without stopping.

We proceeded over to the marching field, where a commanding colonel was preparing to give a speech. We all stood at attention while the cadets were going to pass in review.

The colonel began: "Lieutenants, congratulations and welcome . . ."

Suddenly I heard: "Roddy, Roddy!"

" . . . to the U.S. Army," the colonel continued.

My mother was *shlepping* across the field in front of the whole corps.

"Roddy, I've got five more dollars, I've got five more dollars."

"Mama," I yelled, "Get off the field, or you'll be trampled on!"

Captain Dalquist and all the new officers looked astonished to see a woman with a five-dollar bill held high, slowly stepping across the parade grounds toward me.

The colonel, however, not noticing my mother, ordered the troops to march in her direction. Mama had all but disappeared among the marching heads.; now she was merely a hand, waving money.

"Lieutenant?" Captain Dahlquist said.

I did not respond.

"Lieutenant," he repeated loudly.

"Yes, yes, sir." I was not used to the new appellation.

"Who is that woman on the field, waving a flag?"

"That's my mother," I said.

"Can you tell me why she's being so patriotic?"

"That's not a flag, sir. It's a five-dollar bill."

"Does your mother always act like this?"

"Oh, no, sir."

"Kindly inform her that she is off-limits."

"Roddy, Roddy! I've got the five dollars," Mama yelled, oblivious.

Such was the auspicious beginning to my career. The entire officer corps will long remember Mama as she passed in review.

How I Helped
Defeat Communism

ᴁ

W e finished our training at Fort Bliss without ever again firing those damn guns. I was not a bad officer academically, graduating eleventh in the class. But could I fool the brass in an army unit in the field? As a bona fide second lieutenant, I received my orders for the European command, which meant shipping over to Germany. The Korean War was over. I had won.

In March of 1955, the *S.N. Goethels* docked at Bremerhaven, Germany. As I walked down the gangplank, I was greeted by a flock of screeching seagulls and a babble of chattering Germans, not one of whom would ever admit to fighting on the western front.

I took the train from Bremerhaven to Kaiserslautern. On arrival, I heard my first German words: *Äufsteigen,"* the conductor yelled. Get off.

A corporal in a Jeep drove up to the base, where I saw the first of two signs:

Greetings
25th AAA Battalion
90MM Guns
Kaiserslautern, Germany

And also:

ACHTUNG!
Deutsche Pantzer Kaserne
(German Tank Barracks)
Sieg Heil!

In 1955, Kaiserslautern was a small town of fifty thousand people located in southern Germany. The 25th AAA Battalion, located on the outskirts of the town, was a converted German army *kaserne*, or barracks. A Panzer corps of tanks had been housed there ten years before. As I entered the gates, I could easily imagine ranks of goose-stepping Nazis, now replaced by my *A* platoon of American soldiers marching in time to my first sergeant. He saluted me and gave me the standard operating instructions, my duties as a second lieutenant in the U.S. Army. I read the sheet he handed me.

Responsible for:
Four 90-Millimeter Anti-Aircraft Artillery Guns
Four 50-Caliber Machine Guns
One Radar Van
Short-Arm Inspection

Short-arm inspection? What could that be? I have long thin arms, just like my legs. Could I pass?

I looked up the hill at the four World War II 90mm guns pointing toward the sky as if searching for a Russian MIG.

The sergeant put a sheet of paper in front of me and said, "Here, sign this, sir."

"What am I signing?"

"Oh, just your life away, sir. You're just agreeing that if anything happens to the equipment, you're responsible."

"What's it worth?"

"A million dollars."

"A million? You sign it," I commanded.

"Oh, no, sir. Rank has its privileges. That's why you have the honor of signing it."

I reluctantly signed. How could they ever collect?

The sergeant asked if I wanted to meet the men. My heart

immediately sped up in response to my shy nervous system. Why did I have to meet them? Couldn't I just give them orders?

I marched up to the platoon, the men standing at attention. I paused, put my arms behind my back like General Eisenhower, and said, "Pleased to meet you."

I felt like hitting my forehead with my fist. Pleased? What a lie it was. I was terrified.

I was so shy I had trouble giving orders with a firm tone. My voice squeaked. I could just imagine myself in combat. I would crawl out of my foxhole and howl, "Follow me!" After thirty steps I would look back and see no one. "Follow me, please. Just this once, pleeze."

I was so scared I couldn't say a word. I dismissed the men and walked to the second floor of the barracks and met Captain White, my new commanding officer. He was a spit-and-polish soldier whose shoes were so shiny I could see my face in them. His shirt and pants were taut with heavy starch. He was so neat and clean I thought he was a toy soldier.

His desk was perfect, gleaming, with everything in its proper place. I wiped my belt buckle with my sleeve and brushed my shoes against my pants self-consciously.

"Lieutenant, do you have to go to the bathroom?"

"N-no, sir."

"Well, why are you squirming so much?"

"Uh, just nervous, sir." I began the counting again.

"Have you met the platoon yet?"

My mental counting multiplied: *Four, five, six, six, five, four.*

"There's a problem with this platoon," the captain said. "It's not sharp. They flunked the inspection last year. I want them cleaned up. Here are your orders for tomorrow."

"Yes, sir." I saluted and left.

As I walked down the stairs and out of the barracks, a brilliant idea took shape in my mind. If I wanted to impress the captain I would have to create a unit in the image of my captain — spotless. I longed to succeed in the army. How better than to pass the inspection with distinction? The question arose: how could a born *shlepper* turn World War II *shleppy* guns into polished gems?

I read the orders. I would teach a class on the ballistics of the 90mm gun to the troops. The idea of teaching a class filled me with terror. Rituals popped out: looking back, squinting my left eye, skipping over every crack.

The next morning, as I walked up the steps to the lectern, my hands were clammy and shaking. I reached the stage and faced fifty young enlisted men waiting for the wisdom I would be shoving down their throats. I began with a trembling voice:

"Uhh …uhh-gh-gh-gh. I-I I'm Lieutenant Fadem. I-I'm here to speak uh… uh…. " I forgot the subject. "Uh …uh, where are my notes? Oh, the guns — yes, when you shoot the guns, the shell goes up in a parabolic arc and then curves d-downward, like a curve ball."

Kiss of death, kiss of death. I feared the worst.

Looking up, I noticed that half the men were sleeping. How could I be so nervous when the men couldn't care less? I relaxed and concluded that maybe I could learn something. As I talked about the ballistics of our guns, I realized that our 90mm anti-aircraft artillery could only shoot down a plane flying five hundred miles an hour, but the Russian MIGs flew at six hundred!

After the class, I raced to the captain's office and told him of my great discovery.

The captain looked at me with a surprised look. "Fadem, who do you think you are, some kind of Sherlock Holmes? Of course we can't shoot the MIGs."

"We really can't hit anything?" I asked.

"Well, that's not quite true," he explained. "When we go shoot target practice on the Baltic Sea in June, we'll shoot at the Piper Cub planes flying one hundred miles per hour with a target sleeve extending out from the tail. And I'll have you know we always hit the sleeve, not the plane."

"But what are we doing here, sir?" I asked.

"It's our mission. We're the first line of defense against the Communists."

"You mean we're all that's standing between us and the Communists?"

"It's a new phrase in our jargon, 'The Domino Effect.' If we lose here, everything else goes." It was coined during the French Indochina War. When Dien Ben Phu fell President Eisenhower said it.

I had never heard of the concept before. Who could ever believe such a crazy notion?

THE SHORT-ARM INSPECTION

A Paradise for Mohels

Once a month, I received orders to serve as Officer of the Guard (in charge of anything that occurs overnight at the base. My job was to make the rounds of the base every two hours to check that the guards were not sleeping.

The sergeant had to wake me up out of a deep sleep all night. Once, he woke me up early, pointing a flashlight in my face.

"What's this," I moaned.

"It's for the short-arm inspection."

"What's that?"

"You've got to check the soldier's dicks."

"For what?"

"The clap."

Oy veh, why did I get all the crappy jobs?

"Follow me, sir, and we'll wake up the men. This flashlight will do the trick."

To my surprise, the army required periodic inspections of the soldiers' genitalia during the night. Again, as an officer of lowest seniority, I became the resident schmekel-checker. A sergeant led me through the barracks once a week, armed with a flashlight, shining it on the men as they stood by their beds with their pants down.

Why in the world did the army have its officers check the mens' penises for venereal disease? I was no doctor, I had no clue what I was looking for. I quickly observed a lot of different dangling participles looking up at me: some were shriveled, oblong, round; some suffered from permanent shrinkage; and for the first time I saw an uncircumcised one. *Oy veh.*

The sergeant dutifully led me past the men. Everything was bearable until I arrived before the man the platoon lovingly referred to as "The Salami." His real name was Brodsky, and there, hanging between his legs, was the pride of the Fifth Army and the biggest penis in the European command. With its long foreskin, his schlong looked like a Pig in the Blanket. It was so long he was pronounced persona non grata by the whores in town. Brodsky stood tall and proud, his heckled-shmeckel hanging down to his kneecaps. He was truly a mohel's dream.

"Look, sir," the sergeant said, shining the flashlight right on the salami. "This sure doesn't look normal to me."

I couldn't look it in the eye. I felt safer watching the long shadow it cast on the floor. "What do you want me to do with it?" I said. "I'm no rabbi."

Suddenly the pride of the Fifth Army woke up and stood at attention.

"Inspection over! Pants up! Every man for himself!" I shouted as the sergeant and I ran for the hills, hoping that nothing was coming up from behind.

How I Became Another Clarence Darrow

∽

I received another lesson in the importance of seniority when, after a month in Germany, word came down from battalion headquarters that one officer from each battery would report at 1600 hours that afternoon.

I left for headquarters that afternoon. Colonel White, a sharp-looking man in his fifties, was waiting to talk to a small group of us. In the army, he said, it was necessary to have courts-martial on base or in the field of combat; junior officers, not lawyers, had to act as prosecutor and defense counsels.

"We need strong men to put away the screw-ups," he said. "God knows we have enough of them. And we also need some men for the defense. But remember, our experience shows that ninety percent of those charged are found guilty; the defense counsel really doesn't have to work too hard. Do I have volunteers to act as prosecutors? I want men who are go-getters for this job." All the hands shot up but mine.

"Good," the colonel said. I was looking down when he approached me. "Fadem, you're just the man I'm looking for."

"Who, me?"

"I think you're perfect for the job of defense counsel."

"I'm honored, sir, but I know nothing about the law."

"Exactly the reason I know you'll do well. Here's all you'll need." He handed me the manual: *The Code of Military Justice.* The army has a quaint notion, I realized, that any soldier brought before a court-martial is presumed guilty until proven innocent.

So what's an officer to do? Obey, and put them away.

I had a conscience, though, and I had always thought that every person had a right to a fair trial. Therefore, I began obsessing: *I have to win a case, I have to win a case.* Just like when I received the lieutenant bars, I had to prove I could succeed.

My first case was assault and battery. Assault was easy, but all I knew about battery was the one in my car. Law school was out of the question, just the code manual.

So there I was, mastering the law the night before defending Private Martinez, who was accused of holding an entrenching tool while going from barracks to barracks, searching for Private Hernandez. Both were from Texas and had met in boot camp at Fort Bliss. On that fateful night in Germany, they had a scuffle, and the tool grazed Hernandez's head. I had some of their friends testify that they had horsed around previously and played jokes on each other. This was just another harmless escapade.

My final summation concluded that as the manual said, without fear, there was no battery. That with no fear, no battery, and without threat, no assault. I felt exaltation as I sat down, knowing that even Clarence Darrow would have been proud of me.

The court adjourned for over three hours, which by army standards meant that I had a good chance of winning.

The officers marched in and gave their verdict: "Guilty, six months' pay forfeiture and six months in prison." (Six and six.)

I ran up to the officer of the court, "How could I lose?"

"The entrenching tool," he said. "You forgot intent. He went all over the barracks with an entrenching tool, looking for Hernandez. Now look, you did a good job. In fact, too good for your own good. Don't you get it? You've got the greatest job in the entire U.S. Army. Defense counsel. Don't you like it?"

"Yes, I do, sir."

"There's no pressure on you, the perfect job. All you have to do to succeed is to fail. Your job is to defend them, not get them off. Do you understand?"

"Uh, yes, sir."

"You know what would happen if you got someone off in a court-martial? It would mean you're one hell of a lawyer. Then you're too good for the defense. They'll be forced to make you trial prosecutor. Then you'll know what real pressure is."

I got the message. I would never again throw such passion into my work.

I became known by the troops as "Six and Six." I had become the reliable loser for the defense. AWOL, or absent without leave, were easy convictions. All the prosecution needed was the morning report, showing my client was absent and I knew he was a goner.

The word soon got around that I was tough on crime. I had put fear in the heart of my countrymen. The colonel called and congratulated me for having lowered the crime rate single-handed. I was only doing my duty and according to the army, they were guilty. I was a Clarence Darrow in reverse.

As a reward I was promoted to first lieutenant. I was no longer a *shlepper*. I had finally learned how to succeed in the army. I was a *shlemiel* first class.

The Immaculate Platoon

⟨✏⟩

"And I polished up the handles so carfullee,
That now I am the ruler of the Queen's Nayvee."
— Gilbert & Sullivan and me

The army loves its shiny brass buckles, gleaming boots, and spotless rifles. The military has always had an obsession with spit and polish, especially in peacetime, to such a degree that they would rather shine than shoot. That was fine with me because I could never hit anything anyway.

The captain's gleaming countenance gave me a bedazzling idea: create the shiniest and therefore the most beautiful and best platoon in the battalion. Who cares if we couldn't shoot straight?

I observed the dirty, mud-caked, dull, khaki-colored jeeps, trucks, and guns and decided to transform this dross into gloss. I gathered the men and told them we were temporarily suspending training on the guns and radar, which didn't mean very much anyway. We were going to see who could have the shiniest equipment. I promised a two-day pass if we won an award. The men greeted the news with cheer. I chose Tide, the first choice for my rifle at Ft. Riley.

That night, we washed down everything with the detergent. Then, we poured moisturizer and shampoo on everything and furiously scrubbed like mad Dutchmen. After two days, they were ready for the creme rinse.

We hosed everything down until there arose a Tide-L-Wave of soap suds mushrooming into a glob of bubbles, swirling everywhere, dousing the whole platoon. The bubbles were so wunnerful, wunnerful, I felt like dancing to Lawrence Welk's champagne music.

I wandered out of the white foam, lathered with a soufflé of bubbles. Out of the soapy blizzard came a voice. "Is that you, Lieutenant?"

"Y-yes, sir," I told the captain, blowing bubbles out of my mouth.

"You look like you just got spit out of a washing machine! Where's the platoon?"

"It's all there, sir. We've been cleaning the guns."

Suddenly, large gobs of suds and bubbles surged out of the gun barrels like soapshells. It was great.

The captain stood in amazement.

"We're about finished," I said, "The men are just rinsing the firing mechanisms and the barrels." No sooner had I finished speaking than *whhhoooshh*! A soapshell, without the use of radar, made a direct hit on the captain, right on his nose. I had hit my first bull's-eye.

"Cease fire! Turn those damn guns off!" the captain screeched, turning away.

"Sorry, sir."

"I hope you can shoot them as well as you can clean them!"

"I don't know about that but I *do* remember your telling me how you like a spit-and-polish battery. We're going to show up the whole battalion." Another magnificent obsession.

"You know, Fadem," he said, moping the suds from his brow, "I like the way you talk. I never thought of spit-and-polish guns."

"And jeeps and trucks and radar vans," I added.

"And the mess hall, the barracks, and the bulldozers," he said.

The captain reflected a moment. "This is one of the most brilliant military ideas I've ever heard of. If need be, we can shine 'em, shield 'em, or shoot 'em. I like your initiative, Fadem. You have the making of a great gun platoon commander."

"Thank you, sir."

I felt something swish past my right ear. *Splashh!* Right on his glasses. He was right. We could sure shoot 'em.

After the platoon had cleaned off every piece of equipment, we started staining the guns dark brown. Every enlisted man was required to bring his brush and shoe cloth and start polishing. When they were done, the 90mm guns gleamed so brightly, it seemed to have been a shame to even consider shooting them ever again.

Fate smiled on me the following week. After we polished all the handles and the doors and the floors of the barracks, serendipity walked through the front gate in the form of a once-a-year, unannounced inspection by the brigade commander.

The most feared inspection of all was the unexpected one. Everyone was surprised by the Inspector General's appearance, everywhere except A Platoon. We alone were prepared. The inspectors were astonished at our condition of the equipment and gave us not one "gig" or bad mark. We set the record, received a unit citation, and the men got their weekend passes. I had attained my goal, was at the height of my career; unfortunately, I had nowhere to go but down.

With the help of a few good men, I was transformed into a superficial lieutenant, like the guns that shined. Although I could never be a brilliant fighter, I glistened with confidence about my beautiful guns. But deep down a question haunted me: Could we shoot 90mm shells as we did soapshells? That answer would soon come, but in the meantime I had discovered what the army was looking for with all their emphasis on shiny brass, spit-and-polish shoes and buckles, and beautiful painted guns: I had created the immaculate perception.

I had come a long way, but was I simply lucky or was Shleppriel guiding me from on high? I was content to continue defending poor souls in court and then walk up the ramp to observe my luminous guns. I was feeling cocky, until I soon discovered a banana peel waiting on the next rung of the ladder. That was the day when the captain announced that we had orders to go out on maneuvers.

"Lieutenant, get all the gear together, pack up the trucks, and prepare the guns for travel."

"What's going on?" I said.

"We're going to fire the guns. Isn't that wonderful?"

"No, no. Where are we going?"

"To the Totendorf Gunnery Base on the Baltic."

"No, no, you can't do that."

"What's wrong with you, Lieutenant?"

"The guns, sir, the guns. They're so beautiful and clean. My men have poured their guts into making the 90mm guns shine like gold. You can't, you can't. They're too beautiful to shoot."

He grabbed my arms. "Lieutenant, get ahold of yourself."

"But, but, they're a model for the whole brigade."

"You're obsessed, Lieutenant. Calm down."

Wasn't the whole army obsessed with cleaning everything spic and span? I was only following orders.

"You've got a great platoon here. We're going to show them that we can shoot them as well as shine them."

"Ah, that we could hit anything," I sighed.

How I Almost Shot Down
My First Plane

$\mathcal{I}\!\mathcal{O}$

Once a year, we would go by convoy up the Autobahn through Mannheim and Hanover, until the highway ended and we proceeded by smaller roads past Kiel and Travemünde, to the firing base at Totendorf on the beaches of the Baltic Sea.

We secured the radar van about one hundred yards from the sea while the four guns were put down right on the beach. I couldn't wait to see how well our shined guns would do. We commenced firing and lo and behold, we were hitting the target, a trailing silvery sleeve being towed by an army plane circling the area.

Out of the blue the radar which was tracking the target began moving toward the tail of the plane! Oh, my God, don't shoot, don't shoot. *Pow-w-w*, the guns blazed. I was afraid to look. We had a perfect cluster of exploding shells around the tail of the plane. What if we hit it? What would they do to me? Was my luck running out?

Suddenly I heard the pilot excoriating us. "You dumb son of a bitch, bastard, fuckhead!" He went on with his scurrilous epithets for a full two minutes. "…no good, rotten morons, imbeciles, cretans, horses' asses. …You dumb shits. You trying to shoot me down?"

"Hell, no! We couldn't shoot anything down," I radioed back. The pilot was acting as though we had actually hit him. But he should have known better. We couldn't hit anything. We never could hit a MiG, but we almost shot down our own plane.

After having shot four out of ten target streamers and a near miss on one of the target planes, the 25th AAA Battalion set out to return to base. We had fulfilled our mission. The unit could shoot a 90mm gun as well as I could fire a carbine.

We packed all the weapons in twelve trucks and headed out with the radar van in front. The convoy proceeded with the usual army discipline, fifty feet between trucks, lights on, and me in a jeep halfway back. We passed Travemünde, Kiel, and headed south to the Autobahn.

As I looked down the road, I noticed a peaceful railroad crossing ahead. As the radar van approached the crossing guards started to descend. The guard rails kept coming down. The van sped up. Growing alarmed, I ordered my driver to drive past the trucks ahead of me. As the gates came down, I started yelling, "Stop! Stop! Can't they see the crossing? Slow down. Oh, my God, they're trying to beat the signal!"

Crashhhhhhhhhhhhhhhhhhhh!!!

The guard rail split in two. The radar van crumbled and went off the side of the road and toppled over.

The rest of the convoy stopped, and a gaggle of Germans ran out of the nearby village, loudly barking *auf* Deutsch. *"Was is los?"* (What's the trouble?)

"Was is passiert?" (What happened?)

I found the burgermeister, and with my limited knowledge of German learned that the mayor wanted compensation. He had papers to be filled out, and the estimate was two hundred U.S. dollars.

The captain drove up and I reassures him. "Sir, sir, it's okay. The guard crossing can be fixed for two hundred dollars."

"Lieutenant, look over there." The captain pointed at the radar van.

"Where? Oh, you mean that. It can be repaired too, sir."

"Yes, for two hundred thousand U.S. dollars. It's a wreck."

"Sorry, sir."

"Lieutenant, do you know who signed for this formerly magnificent technology?"

"I ... I ... I did?"

"Yes, and that makes you responsible for two hundred thousand U.S. dollars."

My anxiety rose so high I thought my blood pressure would pop my head. I kept repeating, "I'm innocent, I'm innocent." How could I ever have signed that paper? How could I defend myself? No, no way. If I acted as my own lawyer, I would be locked up without a key. They thought about court-martialing me, but decided to promote me to captain and dock my pay to pay for the radar van. But alas, my army time was up and I had to leave the service in six weeks. That $200,000 debt became the beginning of our trillion-dollar deficit.

CALL ME SHLEMIEL

◦

"I have tasted command, I cannot give it up."

— Napoleon

I knew I had reached my level of incompetence. The army tried to trade me to the Russians for a commie to be named later, but the deal fell through. They concluded the favorite place to put an army screw-up was in a cushy post. Although I couldn't boil an egg, much less make an omelette, they made me mess officer. The only thing I had going for me was that I was a mess.

The first thing I did was find the mess sergeant and tell him how much I liked his cooking. All I asked was there be few complaints and that nobody got sick. He was my cooking representative.

But I had to find something to do. The men might think I was some kind of turkey if I just sat on a stove all day. I thought back to Sergeant Haman at Fort Riley and his inspection finger. "If you try hard enough, you can always find a speck of dust," he said. So, I decided to march into the mess hall with my index finger at attention. Gently inspecting every pot, pan, and kettle, I also anointed myself Official Food Tester for the 25th AAA Battalion. I would go around and taste a little egg, a bit of bacon, and (ugh) SOS (Shit on a Shingle, a common army dish made with bacon and a thick white sauce). My only advice about army food came from my father: add more pepper and then a little more. In no time at all, the officers and soldiers began to comment favorably on how tasty the mess had become. And as clean as a rifle bore.

But I was no longer a commander in the artillery. As Napoleon would have put it, I had felt the exaltation of command, and I was reluctant to relinquish it. But how could I go on? I was following in the footsteps of the little Corsican by rapid promotion. If I could have been allowed to keep screwing up, who knows what I might have become?

Now, as mess officer for the battalion, how could I achieve momentous victories in Europe? No Austerlitzes were left for me to conquer. The Austrians were our friends now. All that was left for me was to defeat the Russians and make the world safe from communism. I could begin my invasion with a barrage of rotten eggs followed by a frontal bayonet assault with knives and forks. Led on by my inspection finger and a warm coat, I could have in no time been gorging myself on Chicken Kiev in Moscow. I felt like Napoleon II, das Schlepper on the Rhine

Knowing my two years were up, I had a strange mixed feeling about leaving the army. On the one hand I was happy to be getting out; on the other, I felt this strange affinity to the army, to its regimen, its compulsive need for order, always saluting and its obsession with repeating things each hour of the day. The army was one big OCD-obsessive compulsive dis-order.

Whatever my problem was, I didn't like change. I felt comfortable with the repetitious nature of a day in the army. What bothered me was the uncertainty of the future. Going home — to become what? I packed my suitcase, shined my shoes, and put on my neatly pressed civilian clothes. As I left the entrance gate, I raised my head, picked up the pace, and began quietly singing Gilbert and Sullivan to myself:

I cleaned the windows and I swept the floors,
And I polished up the guns and cleaned the bores.
I polished up the guns so carefullee,
So I could have become the Ruler of the U.S. Armee.

I had succeeded in the army and helped defend the country from Communism. We eventually won, but no one ever thanked me.

The first part of my odyssey was over, and the wandering Jew would return home, a first class *shlemiel* lieutenant. Mama, Pop, and all the relatives *kvelled* over me. Aunt Lena had us over for dinner, and I felt so nostalgic seeing Pop sipping his bourbon before falling asleep with a snore. Mama was happy in her special Sunday clothes. What a pleasure, *shnoring* again.

Pop asked about my army experiences, and I told him quite proudly what kind of great lawyer I had been without any training at all. I didn't have the nerve to mention to a marine that I could never qualify with the rifle.

Napoleon II — Das Schlepper on the Rhine

NUMBERS

I came home the conquering hero, but I was really like the Jews wandering in the wilderness of the desert in the book of Numbers in the Bible. I had no idea what path I would take in life. Although I had made vast strides as a leader, a Napoleon of the army and a zestful mess officer, I still couldn't make a living in civilian life. I had no choice but to return to my room next to my parents' snoring and arguing.

Mama was relieved and began obsessing over her favorite subject, mingling. She pushed me to mix and go to parties. "Don't you like girls?"

Of course I liked girls. I just didn't like calling them.

I wanted to find a girl and a job at the same time. Neither would be easy. Armed with my liberal arts degree, I applied to many of the leading companies in St. Louis. Each one turned me down. Personnel officers even held my studies of French, German, and Russian against me. Sorry, they would say, but they had no plans to opening offices in Paris, Berlin, or Moscow. I tried small corporations. Gun stores went ballistic when they heard I couldn't shoot a gun. Nobody wanted me.

I went home to mope and was promptly surprised by a phone call. I heard what sounded like a flock of singing birds perched on the telephone lines.

"Are you still reading dirty comic books?" a canary chirped at me.

"Dov! Is that you?" I said.

"You were expecting Meyer Shwab?"

"What have you been doing?"

"Well, I'm still studying the Bible in my spare time. Now, I'm working for my father's brokerage house. I'm in accounting and boy, do I hate it. I heard you needed a job?"

"Yes, but how'd you know?"

"Let's say a little birdie told me. My father is looking for a broker-trainee. He runs a small regional brokerage house. Are you interested? You'll start at four hundred dollars a month."

I gulped. "But I don't know anything about the brokerage business."

"Precisely what my father's looking for. Someone with a fresh mind whom he can train."

He sounded like the colonel back in Germany saying what a great defense counsel I would make with no knowledge of the law.

"What do I have to do?" I asked.

"Nothing."

"Great, I'm your man."

As the good book says, I would, for the rest of my financial career, deal with "Numbers."

WHERE ANGELS FEAR TO TRADE

◎

"A cynic is one who knows the price of
everything and the value of nothing."
— timeless advice from Oscar Wilde
concerning Internet stocks

I've always wanted to be a stand-up comedian but was too shy; so I became a sit-down comic stockbroker. If I gave a loser, I gave a joke. If I gave a second loser, I gave a second joke. A third loser, and no one was laughing, buying, or selling.

My first day in the brokerage business was similar to my first experience in the army. I was once more the round peg in the square hole. Dov's father, who also had a bird's nose, sat me down with a phone and a phone book and said, "Call everybody you know, don't know, and never care to know."

"What do I say?"

"Everything, anything and nothing. Promise them the moon, but sell them our deals. You got it?"

"Yes, yes, sir, but how many calls do I have to make?"

"Just a hundred a day!"

"Is that all?" I asked.

"You want to make two hundred? I like your initiative, Fadem, you've got the makings of a great broker."

I looked around and saw an old-timer with a wizened, scarred face, who had survived the 1929 crash. He, like the veteran brokers of today, couldn't understand the high-priced glamorous stocks, which remain an eternal enigma. No matter how hard he tried to forget seeing people jump out of windows, he never left the building without first looking up.

Strolling around, I noticed many middle-aged brokers with cluttered desks, who also happened to have cluttered minds. The younger account executives, with clean desks, weren't doing any business.

I couldn't stand the methodical broker who set a daily goal for himself — say five thousand shares a day. He usually got nervous by the end of the day without an order. You could find him feverishly scanning his address book, humming, "Whom Can I Churn To?"

But I still had to make those damn phone calls. If you think I've had trouble calling girls you can imagine the horror of making cold calls to prospects. I felt as if I were auditioning for hell. To avoid the pains, I would spend the days talking to my friends. Occasionally, they felt sorry for me and gave me an order. I was again like a *shlepper* in the army, wanting to attain success in a field for which I was totally unfit.

I had only one solution: wait for the customer to call me. This was a most heretical position on Wall Street. By 1965, the pressure was on to produce. I had to find a better way. Oh, God, can't You help me? A tip? A glimpse of the future? No, that's asking too much. I'll make one more cold call that even the Almighty might applaud for *chutzpah.* I'll cold call God. I looked in the phone book, but all I could find was Lord and Taylor. So I went back to my daydreaming.

I had no choice but to muddle through finding customers. I left my card everywhere I went. I loved Chinese food so I went two to three times a week to Chu Chin Chow's restaurant, where finally the owner began to recognize me. I always praised his food and left my card. One night he watched me screwing up with the chopsticks, one stick almost went up my nose and the other almost poked me in the eye. He ran over to show the traditional Chinese way to prevent me from hurting myself.

He sat down and we discussed chopsticks, hot stocks, chow mein, and his prized hard noodles in his chow mein. The one thing he worried about was his own noodle, which was rarely hard. I told him I couldn't help him in that department, but as a stockbroker I sure could help him make a fortune cookie.

My new Chinese friend called so often that I didn't know whether to call him Chu, Chin, or Chou. I settled on "Charlie with the limp noodle."

"How market?" he said.

"Down," I said.

"Down hard?" he asked.

"No, just a soft landing."

"Just like noodle," he moaned.

But Charlie had a problem common to investors — his emotions. Price was the prime mover of his emotions. If stocks were soaring, he could only buy after a big move. Then if stocks were plummeting he could sell in fear. I could only think of Shakespeare:

"To buy or not to buy, that is not the question.

When to sell is always the problem."

My favorite customer was Herman Winkler, whom I met at the JCCA Health Club. One day I was performing one of my ritual tics, winking my left eye, when I noticed a balding middle-aged guy sitting directly across from me winking back at me. At first, I thought he was making a pass at me, but I soon realized that he, too, had a tic. We were playing a game of Tic-Toc-Two.

He called himself Wink, and it was his way of saying hello to a fellow winker. He had found a kindred soul with whom he was looking for someone to share his troubles. When I told him I was a broker, his open eye gleamed as he said at last he had found someone he could trust. He became my best customer, but I had to listen to all his complaining that his wife demanded sex once a year. So, was it his fault he had an assortment of girlfriends who always happened to be shiksehs? He always winked hard when he mentioned one. What did I care? The more he complained, the more stocks he bought.

Time passed, and I gradually learned the art of being a successful broker. The customers, in their infinite naiveté, thought brokers had a crystal ball. Unfortunately, we don't, so we pretend. In the tradition of the Oracle of Delphi, I made all kinds of vague predictions and warnings about the future course of the market. At the same time, I would watch the market gurus on television and pick up tips on clairvoyance.

"Where do you think the market is heading?" a customer would ask.

"Oh, I think it'll trade in a broad trading range," I'd say. Translation: The market's going up and down, but I have no idea where it'll wind up.

Or, "It'll be definitely volatile, and you must be selective." Translation: Whichever way the market goes, you sure as hell better pick the right stock, or you'll lose your fanny. "I think the Dow's going up to twelve thousand this year." Translation: Pick a number, the higher the better. If you're right, you're a genius; if not, they probably won't remember you were wrong. As far as predicting the Dow-Jones average, only God knows, and He's not talking.

If you're going to be a guru, always be bullish. No matter how bad the market drops, always call it a "correction." Because the market goes up two thirds of the time, you'll eventually be right.

The phone rang. "Yes, Nancy," I said to my secretary.

"I'm sorry to interrupt you, but I have someone on long distance who demands to talk to you. He won't give his name, but he says he's from. . . ."

"Yes, yes."

"Heaven!"

"What?" I switched back over.

God did hear me. For the first time since Moses, he was calling me.

"Hello, is this the Lord?"

"No, it's Shleppriel."

"Oh, you need some investment advice?"

"No. I have an order from God."

Then I heard stentorian commands:

The Ten Commandments
Of a Broker

I Thou shalt not sell *dreck (crap)*.

II Thou shalt not lie, but never admit the truth.

III Thou shalt not bear false prophecy.

IV Thou shalt not take the name of Greenspan in vain.

V Thou shalt not worship false Gods and G-urus.

VI Thou shalt not sell financial products with the highest commission.

VII Thou shalt not covet thy colleagues' commissions, his clients, nor his secretary.

VIII Thou shalt always protect thyself, and if there is any time left over, do thy job.

IX Thou shalt honor all thy best clients with hot new issues.

X If thou canst buy all you want of a new issue, you do not want any; if thou canst obtain any, buy all thou can get.

He hung up, and I knew instinctively that I had to make money the old-fashioned way — earning money for my customers. I was no longer a big grosser. I had to put the customers' interest before my principal.

"Ours was not to sell or buy, ours was but to reason why" was my new motto.

I promised myself from now on every sale I make will be a *mitzvah*. If only I could make a living. My new card would read:

Rodowe W. Fadem
Stockbroker

"Clients Restricted to Menshes"

I would continue for decades in the business. Old brokers never die, they just yield to maturity.

God's Gift to Shiksehs

ॐ

"A shikseh, a shikseh, my kingdom for a shikseh."
— Richard III and Rodowe Fadem II

I went out with many Jewish girls, but none of them considered me a prize package. The better looking the girl or the more expensive her home, the cooler was my welcome. One rich girl and her mother actually interviewed me in the kitchen of their palatial mansion before she (probably from the urging of her mother) informed me that she would be busy for the next twenty years. Other times, a girl would give me a Friday night date as an audition for a Saturday night, which never came. For me, Saturday night was the loneliest night of the week.

But then my favorite customer, Wink, who always winked when he made a sexual allusion, called.

"Have I got a deal for you," he said.

"You're calling me at home because you've got a hot stock?"

"Oh, no, I've got a hot honey."

"A honey?"

"Yes, a hot, beautiful *shikseh* who wants to meet you." I knew he was winking.

"Me?"

"Well, you know my girlfriend Gloria? She told her girlfriend, a Catholic, how wonderful Jewish men are, and I told her about you.

"But why me?"

"Because you're Jewish, and *shiksehs* think we're the greatest things since chopped liver."

"Gee," I said in awe as I contemplated my first date with a live fantasy. What a wonderful *mitzvah* — to be God's gift to *shiksehs*."

I called Mary and found her so friendly, bubbly, and available any night. I picked her up at her small apartment and we went to a movie. I couldn't believe it. Was she my Aphrodite, the goddess of love? Or Helen of Tr-*oy*, the *shikseh* that launched a thousand ships? Shockingly, she placed her hand on mine and was actually looking at me with longing eyes. I leaned over and kissed those lovely lips. My heart revved up, my pulse soared as I embraced her. My high school dream had come true. I had tasted the nectar of a goddess and I was thoroughly spellbound.

For the next three weeks I could not get her out of my mind. I was in seventh heaven, drifting on cloud nine, high above Mount Olympus.

Then Wink called and punctured my dream.

"I just talked to Mary and she said you're going steady."

"What's wrong with that?"

"I told you to take her out, not marry her."

"For the first time, Wink, I think I'm in love," I said.

"Love, shmove," he said, "you're infatuated with a dream. We all want *shiksehs*, but anything that's too good, we can't have. Look, she's just a country girl and wants a husband and someone gave her the clue."

'What clue?"

"That Jewish boys make the finest husbands, that they know we make great fathers, provide well for them, and we don't beat them."

"Is that so bad?"

"It's one thing to *shtoop* [have sex with] them, but it's another to marry them. She's a Catholic, not that there's anything wrong with being a Catholic. We're just not meant for each other, and besides, your parents will consider you dead if you did such a thing."

"Really?" I thought back to the time when Mama yelled in the phone when she thought my brother was talking to a *shikseh*, who turned out to be a typist.

But I was still smitten by the gods, until one night. Mary, in her celestial fashion, asked how I liked being a stockbroker.

"Oh, it's exciting," I said.

"Is it financially rewarding?" she said.

"Oh yes, I'm making six hundred a month now and hope to do more next month."

"Gee, that's fantastic. By the way, do you want to be a Jew all your life?"

"*Oy vey-h-h,*" I moaned as I felt myself tumbling off the heights of Mount Olympus. The spell was broken. My goddess had a fatal flaw; she talked too much. I had discovered that my Aphrodite was a mere mortal.

My life as God's gift to *shiksehs* was over. I had no choice but to offer myself to the Jewish girls of the world. I had to enter that painful experience reminiscent of the inquisition. I had to enter a new world called:

The Trauma of Dating

The meek shall inherit the earth, but they sure don't make out in it. If love affairs are made in heaven, then my Guardian Angel had let me down.

I tormented myself just looking at the phone. What if she rejects me? What if she accepts? Equally horrible, I would finally force myself to dial, each time hanging up before someone picked up the phone. Sometimes I let it ring until a female voice answered. "Sorry, wrong number," I would say, hanging up. Or, if I had the nerve, "Th-th-this is R-Rod F-ad. Oh, you wouldn't ant to go out with me, would you? No, I guess not."

Being shy wasn't bad enough, but I was a lover who simply didn't like to mingle at house parties, bars, and wedding receptions. I didn't like having to go to any gathering. My greatest delight occurred when someone did not invite me to a wedding. I always politely sent a thank you note.

Mama was obsessed with my social life. Once when I had two friends over to play Monopoly, she burst into the room and blurted out, "Why don't the three of you go out on a double date?"

Mingling was always a problem. Liking neither house parties nor bars, I had to depend on the enmity of strangers for the blind date. My friends meant well, but in fixing me up they were usually nearsighted and I wound up blindsighted.

I resumed life in my old room where I remained until 1968 at the age of thirty-six, when I finally concluded the time had arrived to grow up. I decided to get an apartment. I told Mama the great news, and all she could say was, "Mickie, where did I go wrong?"

I found an apartment in the suburbs and devoured all the women's decorating magazines like *Better Homes and Gardens* and *Good Housekeeping*. I considered contemporary, modern, country, and French provincial, but settled for ultra gauche. I had a vision of something new, exciting, a unique apartment that would set a new standard for urban living and would also serve as a test for a future wife. Thick, red fur carpeting covered the living room floor. On it was a wrap around purple velour sofa with orange naugahyde chairs. All these pieces and lampshades were adorned with plastic covers so I never needed to clean them.

In the bedroom, I had dark blue fur rugs beneath a king-sized bed and a ceramic elephant tile table decorated with big flowers. For a cool effect, a panther poster with its mouth wide open and eyes glowing in the flickering of a lava lamp. To top it off I hung a velvet Elvis poster on the orange wall. I put the *Wall Street Journal* down on the kitchen floor so I could check my portfolio while I fixed myself cereal for breakfast, lunch, and dinner.

Cooking was a disaster. I couldn't boil an egg without turning it into a rock. I tried to broil a hot dog, but it came out a petrified cigar. The house was a mess. I was forced to hire a maid. Though grateful for the money, she quit after a week. Desperate, I had no choice but to seek a wife.

Unfortunately, I had to depend on some of my so-called friends, who were so shortsighted they fixed me up with a midget who was four feet, six inches small. Her name was Sonya Heifetz and she wasn't bad-looking for a dill pickle. We went out to dinner and dancing at a classy place in East St. Louis.

She wore extremely high heels and a hairdo coiffed one-foot high. I bent over and asked Sonya to dance, and she, not wanting to be embarrassed by her height, climbed up on my toes. As a former officer and a gentleman, I could not show my pain. Besides, I was preoccupied with her coiffed hair, which kept poofing up into my nostrils, causing me to sneeze to the beat of the music.

I could not bear the trauma of dating anymore. I needed someone to come and show me the way.

I was tired of calling girls, so I waited for someone to call and fix me up. Sure enough, one of my myopic friends called and told me she met a lovely girl at a wedding reception who was an interior decorator. He swore she was witty, intelligent, and had a bubbly personality. In other words, she probably was not a great beauty.

I was dallying, as usual, trying to have the courage to ask her out. Suddenly, the telephone rang, disturbing my lonely universe.

"Hello, this is Sarah Goldman. My aunt told me that we both had a lot in common. She told me you were about to call, but I said to myself, oh, silly, why not call him and ask if he'd like to go to a party Saturday night."

I was taken aback by her asking for a date just two days in advance. Most Jewish boys like a week or two to decide. Such *chutzpa* (nerve.)

"Well," I said, "I am very busy. (It had been two months since I had a date.) But you know, you sound so nice I'll switch my Saturday night plans to Friday."

"Oh, you're so sweet," she said.

"Do you mind driving? My eyes are kind of bad."

"No problem," she said.

What really bothered me was a professional interior decorator visiting my apartment. I thought it was in good taste, but how could I account for hers? I had to keep her out until I had it thoroughly steam cleaned.

"Do you mind if I wait outside? I'm having some work done and it's caused a bit of a mess."

"Oh, don't worry. That'll be fine. See you Saturday at 6:30."

Fort Riley in the Air

Sarah picked me up and I was pleasantly surprised. She was an almost attractive brunette. She was no beauty, mind you, but I was no prize package either. She was provocatively *zaftig* (Rubenesque) which meant she was probably a good cook (I sure could have used a good meal).

We drove out to St. Charles, out past a boat-shaped restaurant called Noah's Ark.

"You're going to just love this party in the open air," Sarah said.

"You mean the party's outdoors?"

"Yes. See, right ahead. There it is." She pointed straight ahead.

I couldn't believe it, a nemesis from my past came back to persecute me. A hay ride. "Oh no," I screamed.

"What's the matter?"

"Hay, wheat, I'm allergic to all that crap."

"You're kidding, aren't you?" Sarah said.

"I could barely breathe at Fort Riley, Kansas, when I was in the army."

We reached the hay wagon, and I started wheezing.

"What was that?" she asked.

"That was me."

We finally climbed aboard.

"Now, isn't this fun?" she said.

"Agh-h-h-h," I breathed.

"You OK?"

I started coughing. Once aboard, I immediately felt a heaviness in my chest.

"Isn't it romantic?"

"Aghh . . . aghhh . . . yes," I wheezed.

She threw some hay in the air. "I just love romping in the hay, don't you?"

"Aghhh. . . ." I whispered.

All around me people were making out. Seeing this was my big chance, I embraced her, and our lips met in the bliss.

"Ah. . . ahh. . . choo!" I sneezed right in her face. Sneezing and wheezing, I crawled toward the edge of the cart, gasping for fresh air. I was hyperventilating. I found fresh air, I fell off the side onto the ground.

Sarah, wiping her face, quickly jumped to my side.

"Oh, baby, I'm so sorry."

Sarah helped me up and held my arm as I slowly limped toward the car. "Come on," she said, "we'll drive by your apartment and you can lay down on your couch for awhile."

"Oh no, you don't have to come in. Just let me off, I'll be all right." I pleaded, "I haven't had time to clean up. I came home late."

"Oh, don't be so silly. So what if you left a few things lying around? What do you think, I'm some kind of perfectionist?"

She drove me home. We entered the apartment in the dark, and she helped me over to the sofa. I calmed down, bent over, and she undid my shirt.

"I'm much better, thank you," I said.

"Oh, I'm so relieved." She got up, shook her hair a little, and wiped her brow before she turned on the light.

"E-e-e-e-e-owwww!" she screamed, falling back and almost losing her footing.

The howl resounded so loudly in my ears I thought the hound of the Baskervilles was haunting my apartment.

"Oh, my God!" She screamed. "What is this mess? How can you live like this?"

"I - I like it."

"What are all these *Wall Street Journals* doing on the floor? And all the dishes and glasses on the counter? Don't you ever wash them?"

"They're stuck on the counter."

"Let me help you," she said.

Opening the closet, she pulled out a broom, a mop, and a box of Tide. She rolled up her sleeves and went to work. Without a doubt, Sarah was the best maid I ever had. She grabbed the glasses on the counter, yanking at them with all her might.

"What did you do to these glasses?" she asked as she moved on to the sink, where the dishes were piled two inches higher than her head. She looked down at the disposal and gasped. "There's something sticking out. It's . . . it's a dead snake! No, ugh!" she gasped as she confronted my tattered black sock.

"Oh that," I said. "It's an old sock, I don't need it anymore."

"What's this?" she asked. She was cleaning the oven. She got a tissue and picked out what looked like some kind of fossil.

"It's a petrified hot dog."

She was shaking her head as she walked into the bedroom. The moan I heard was like the call of the wild. "An Elvis Presley poster?" She cleaned up and got out of the bedroom as fast as possible. Throughout my apartment she scrubbed the floor, vacuumed the carpeting and, after an hour, had turned my antediluvian cesspool into a pristine jewel. She came back to sit beside me. "Now isn't that better?" she asked.

"Y-yes, I'm feeling better already."

"Ah, poor baby. You're such a mess. You're liable to trip over your own junk or poison yourself on your own cooking. You need someone to take care of you."

"I do?"

"Yes, me."

I was shocked to see her looking at me with adoring eyes. She seemed relieved that her furious housecleaning had rescued me from my den of iniquity. I couldn't understand why she liked me so much. Here I had grown up so shy, so insecure that I couldn't imagine anyone ever loving me for myself.

She cleaned the refrigerator last, throwing out the shriveled brown bananas and the fuzzy, green turkey. "What's a green earmuff doing in the fridge?" she yelled.

"What earmuff?" I asked. "That's cheese."

After she finally finished, she poured herself a glass of milk and came over to sit beside me on the sofa. "There, isn't that better?" She held up the glass of milk. "Here's to us."

"No! No!" I cried. "Don't drink that."

It was too late. "B-f-f-f-f-f-t-t-t!" She blew out the tainted milk all over me. After doing so much for my apartment, Sarah had soured on the milk of human kindness.

Having thoroughly cleaned my abode, Sarah was quite eager to show off her own, and I was curious how a person with a degree in interior design decorated her own place.

She opened the door, her eyes beaming with grand expectations, and turned on the lights. Suddenly, as if a flashbulb exploded in my face, a phantasmagoria of colors — red, coral, blue, even orange — paraded before me. I saw a plethora of red walls and gold brocades, a phalanx of calico prints and an avalanche of floral streamers, waterfalls and mountains. I felt I was going to fall off one of them or throw up.

"*Oy,* veh," I said, placing my hand on my forehead. An interior decorator with bad taste.

"Takes your breath away, doesn't it?" Sarah asked.

"That's it, exactly. I feel a little vertigo, though. Everything seems to be swirling around me."

"Here, sit down on my newly upholstered, orange La-Z-Boy chair."

I eased down into the orange gaucheness of the chair and

almost barfed.

Sarah brought me some cold water. "What's the matter?" she asked.

"Oh, I guess I'm overwhelmed by it all."

"Now just lay back and relax and let my green star-studded walls sooth your nerves," Sarah urged.

"Green? Where are the green walls?" I wondered.

"All around you, just look up," she said proudly.

I looked up, down, over and around. "Looks as red as an overripe tomato to me," I said.

"It can't be. It can't be. I picked the paint out myself." She paused momentarily. "It's really not green?" she said slowly.

"Nope."

"I can't believe it," she insisted.

"What about the green mat by the door, the bindings of the books on the shelves, and the silk pillow on the sofa cushion?" she asked.

"All red," I said.

"You mean, I-I'm color blind?"*

"It could be worse, you could be blind." I smiled at her.

"It's the end of my career! In all these years, no one ever questioned me." She obviously dealt with people who had worse taste than hers. I offered to be her eyes. I realized that some miracle had brought us together, a *shlepper* without a clue about interior decorating and a professional decorator who couldn't see straight. In no time at all, we were engaged.

The next day, Sarah insisted that we exchange engagement gifts. She thought I would be happy with a gross of handkerchiefs so that I would no longer drop my tissues on her shiny floor. In turn, all she wanted in the world was a Hermes black

* According to a leading ophthalmologist, one in twenty men are color blind; in women, one in two hundred.

leather purse with matching leather shoes.

She soon returned and proudly said, "What do you think of my beautiful purse and shoes? Isn't the leather scrumptious? It's just like interior decorating, when you redo one room, the rest looks decrepit. So, I figured you wouldn't mind if I picked myself up a pair of leather gloves and something to make me feel less naked."

"What could that possibly be?"

"Look, silly, a beautiful full-length black leather coat."

She put it on and simply sighed with ecstacy as she felt the leather. This was the beginning of one of the great leather collections in history. Forty-eight leather shoes and thirty-six leather purses. I would learn one day that leather would play a curious role in Princess Sarah's life.

A Marriage Made in Heaven

"Tis better to have loved and lost
than never to have loved at all."

— Elizabeth Taylor and I

I should have been in my beloved "seventh heaven," but I suddenly felt fear. Of what? Would I be a good husband? Would my repetitive thoughts and rituals drive her crazy? Would Sarah go on the pill or would I be forced (ugh) to go back to the drugstore and ask for a prophylactic?

Here, after all these years, I had made a connection with someone to share my life. For one who had always felt unworthy of love I should have been on cloud nine, but the closer I got to the wedding, the more uncomfortable I felt. New thoughts intruded: *What if I don't perform on my wedding night? How could I face the humiliation?*

Should I tell Sarah about the repetitive thoughts slashing at my mind? How could I? And the rituals? Would she think I was crazy? But just like with my parents, I could not tell her. I felt I was being deceitful, a fraud. But I could not help myself.

I vowed I would tell her on a certain night. I would lean over toward her on her couch, intent on spilling out my *kishkas* (guts)! But my heart always sped up, my hands shook, got clammy, and the horrible thoughts surfaced: *Kiss of death, kiss of life, kiss of death, kiss of life,* restrained me, embarrassed me from uttering a word.

Sarah looked at my eyes. She raised her hand and gently caressed my cheek and said, "Poor honey, you haven't been with me for thirty seconds, your eyes glazed over. Where were you, in some other world?"

"Oh, forgive me," I said. "I must have been daydreaming. I must confess I have a few foibles. That's one of them."

"Oh, that okay, honey. If that's the worst thing about you, I can live with that."

I felt guiltier than ever, but the wedding must go on. We plunged into that miserable prelude to connubial bliss: the planning of the wedding.

Sarah kept insisting on green decorations, but she meant red. She wanted pink for the bridesmaids, but picked out crimson. The purple for the tuxedos of the groom and his entourage turned out to be yellow when she picked them out. She wanted blue for the bridesmaids, but picked something close to salmon color. Poor Sarah, she couldn't see straight, so I straightened her out and we ordered purple for the tuxedos and blue for the dresses.

"Whose rabbi will marry us, yours or mine? Should I put down black, white, or blue dishes on the bridal registry? The seating at the tables. . . ."

But then began the all-out frantic assault on my mind. Whose rabbi will we use, my reform or her conservative? Why not invite an orthodox one and cover all the spiritual bases for our union? The hotel, the hotel. Sometimes you have to book it a year in advance. The seating at the reception; you can't have people who can't stand each other sitting next to each other. They'd be like oil and water.

Ten, nine, eight, seven, one, two, three, four, kiss of life, kiss of death, kiss of life, kiss of death. Why can't I get a life? To be or not to be. To have black dishes or not have black dishes. Who puts down black dishes for the bridal registry? Oh, maybe white, maybe red. My poor Sarah was turning into my Hamlet. She simply couldn't make up her mind.

Now I'm five, now I'm ten. Kindergarten was better than the anxiety of a wedding. One day, my pent-up frustrations blew. I yelled out, "Stop already, for God's sake, make up your mind."

Amazingly, she did. What a relief. Now all I had to drive me crazy was the wedding itself. We chose the Colony Hotel. As I, my brother, and my father put on our purple tuxedos, my heart palpitated awaiting the defining moment. A crowd of over two hundred people assembled in the ballroom of the hotel in downtown Clayton, a well-to-do suburb of St. Louis.

Tall candlesticks topped with white tapers and wrapped with ferns lined both sides of the main aisles, where a long white runway stretched to the *bema* or marriage altar.

With a nervous gait, I entered from the side and awaited the parade of bridesmaids who preceded my smiling bride, being escorted by her father.

As she neared me, I felt absolutely petrified, the anxious repetitive thoughts raging in my mind. All the intrusive thoughts of the previous years swirled around my head, as if they were all vying for attention at the same time. A maelstrom of neurons was howling through my head. Richard Wagner's "Here Comes the Bride" did nothing to ease my anxieties.

When Sarah arrived next to me, I was feeling cold. She grabbed my hand and said, "Your hand feels ice cold!" Good thing she couldn't feel my veins.

The rabbi (a reform one we finally agreed on) started the ceremony with a prayer, then some polite remarks before getting to the famous question.

"Do you take this woman to be your lawfully wedded wife?" Silence.

I didn't hear a word. A war was raging in my skull. My feelings of love clashed with obsessions of doubt. A hush descended on the audience. They all waited for my response.

Then I heard Shleppriel, my guardian angel, from far away.

"Marriage is a *mitzvah*. According to the *Talmud*, you are not whole until you are married."

I woke up and looked around, and was shocked to see so many people with their mouths wide open. The rabbi was right. What a *mitzvah* it is to have a family with children. I knew it was something I always wanted.

I bellowed, "I DO."

"You must love her very much to be woken from such a deep sleep," the rabbi said, sounding like the preacher in *Brigadoon*. "I now pronounce you man and wife."

We kissed and he showed me the wine glass wrapped in a paper bag to stomp on. It symbolized how in a moment of joy, we must remember the sorrow of the destruction of the temple in ancient days. I raised my foot and brought it down as hard as I could.

"A miss," the rabbi shouted. I was back in the army missing the target again. I aimed my right foot like a 90mm gun and demolished the wine glass. We were married! It was the last time I put my foot down in my married life.

The Affair of the Hair

Murder on the Paris Express

$\mathcal{\infty}$

When we embarked on our honeymoon we had no way of knowing that a horrendous experience would make my hair stand on end. The two-week excursion my bride and I took started with a romantic cruise down the Rhine and culminated in an overnight train ride from Munich to Paris. I still tremble at the memories, especially of our night aboard the Paris Express. Before our trip was over, I would feel like I was traveling in an Agatha Christie mystery.

Sarah and I had little trouble finding our pre-booked train compartment. Due to the late hour, our roommates, three young women and an elderly man, all French speaking, were already in bed. Or, more accurately, in beds. The compartment, measuring no more than three footsteps wide, had two triple-decker bunks. Fully dressed, my wife and I climbed into the vacant upper bunks. The others, apparently seasoned travelers, managed to slither out of their clothes and into nightgowns and pajamas, all while lying flat on their backs beneath the sheets and continued to converse.

Less agile and of a more conservative nature, I loosened my belt and untied my shoes. I also carefully tucked my glasses and partial dental bridge beneath the white sliver of a pillow. Sarah carefully popped out her contact lenses, then fell asleep immediately.

When the compartment lights went out, I dozed fitfully to the rumblings of the train wheels. Toward morning, a piercing shriek awakened me.

"Ee-e-e-e-e!"

The cry was harrowing enough to make one's hair stand on end. Had murder been committed on the Paris Express? I burrowed deeply into the mattress, covering even my head with the sheet.

"*Zut! Zut! Zut! Alors! Quel énorme rat poilu!*" someone shrieked hysterically.

An enormous furry rat, here in our compartment? I understood French well, and I was sure that's what the girl had said. Oh yes, the scream had come from one of the girls in our room. I had easily deduced this fact using the little gray cells so dear to my hero, Monsieur Poirot.

Smash! Cautiously, I peered out from beneath the sheet. In the darkness, I could just make out one of the girls beating something with her shoe.

"*Allez! Ouste! Fous le camp!*" she screeched (Go on! Out! Get out of here!), pounding a brownish blob cowering on the floor. Not until she booted it down the hallway did she calmly return to bed.

My watch said 4:02 A.M. I watched the luminous minute hand. 4:03 …4:04 …4:09. A scream came from further down the corridor. 4:11 … 4:13. A horrendous howl 4:15 … A bashing noise, followed at 4:21 by a wild yell, "*Putain-de-bordel-de merde*" (too filthy to translate), and a loud squeal. A full chorus of wails, then deadly silence.

Morning arrived as a relief. Everyone but my bride and I changed clothes. Though Sarah and I felt terribly disheveled, we tried to make ourselves presentable. I was ready for Paris.

But was I? A strange sensation crept over me. Though fully clothed, I felt naked in front of my fellow travelers. Something was missing. I could feel cool air blowing in from the corridor and over my head. The breeze was too refreshing. Slowly, I placed my hand on my forehead and inched it upward. Oh, my God! My heart pounded as my pulse quickened. Terror shot through my veins. MY PRECIOUS, PRICELESS, FABULOUS HAIR — the "rug" I'd bought shortly after becoming a broker — HAD DISAPPEARED! As far as I knew, only my wife and my toupee maker had known my secret up to now.

I searched all the beds in our compartment, yanked off the sheets, threw pillows into the air and begged my horror-struck wife to look beneath the bunks. Nothing there of any significance, she reported.

Could someone have stolen the love of my life? Surely, only a fool would waste time on my hair when there were pockets to be picked. I felt a bulge on the right side of my head — a broken hair fastener. Aha! *C'est elementaire.* The hairpiece had fallen off when I turned over in my sleep. Together, my bride and I hunted.

"Your hair couldn't have run away," she said.

It was time to turn into Hercule Poirot, who, besides sharing my intellectual capacities for logical deduction, also had an eggshell of a head. We differed only in the little matter of dress. He was fastidious and meticulous about his custom-made suits and shirts, and perfect bow ties, while I, with mustard on my shirts and soup on my ties, was an unfortunate slob.

I could feel Poirot's perfectly groomed handlebar moustache sprouting along my upper lip, prompting me to exchange my glasses for Poirot's favorite Belgian lorgnette.

"Pardon, *Mademoiselle,*" I said to one of our roommates. "I could not help but hear the fracas in our compartment last night. Tell me, were you the one who screamed?"

"Yes. I kicked an ugly, furry rat out the door," she replied.

Adept at interrogation, I asked, "Are you certain it was a rat?"

"*Mais oui, monsieur,* I saw it. I knelt down and got a good look at it before I sent it on its way."

"But, mademoiselle" I said, stroking my mustache, "appearances can be deceiving, *n'est çe pas?*" I squatted to retrieve a strand of hair. "*Voila!* Do you know what this is?" I asked.

"*Oui, monsieur.* It's a hair from that horrible little beast."

"*Regardez, s'il vous plait.* This is a black hair. You described the animal as being brown. Not only that, but the strand is from my toupee, which dropped from my head to the floor during the night. This was no animal you kicked, mademoiselle. That was my hair."

"Oh no, *monsieur.* I cannot believe it."

My mind raced. The train was due in Paris in twenty minutes. Would my hair be restored first? What would I do without it? Imagine Poirot without his moustache or Holmes without his pipe. How could I return to St. Louis with a balding pate?

Entering the corridor and looking down the hallway, I spied another black hair, this one protruding from the carpet. I knocked on the door of a nearby *couchette* and inquired whether anyone had seen something strange last night.

"My good man," said an elderly Englishman with bushy white eyebrows, a neat white moustache, and a monocle in his right eye. "My wife has been wailing uncontrollably for hours."

That would account for the 4:13 howl.

"She had a harrowing experience," he continued, "and I don't think she's up to — "

"That's all right, George. I can talk now," said a stately matron, a handkerchief in her hand. I explained my investigation.

"A large carnivorous animal attacked me when I got up to use the loo," she said with a shiver.

"Pardon, madame, but I think you were perhaps having a *cauchemar,* a nightmare, as we say in France."

"No, no, I was not dreaming. Here, look at this." She opened her purse and pulled out a long brown hair. "This was not a dream, I assure you. I plucked it from the beast."

"*Oy,*" I said to myself. What a revolting development. Then, spying a luxurious fur coat laying across the bunk, I picked up the sleeve. "You see, madame, your hair obviously came from your own coat."

"You bald-headed twerp." Madam's eyes bulged with anger. "You are no detective. I tell you, a big, bloody rodent came at me. Now get out of here before I crown you with my handbag."

Evidamment the hairy rat/rodent had proceeded down the corridor, gaining bulk and ferocity with each step. I hurried toward the last *couchette,* and found an old woman inside, wearing a faded blue bonnet, a cigar clenched between her lips, and an oddball necklace dangling on her chest. She knitted with two giant needles, one gold and one red.

For a clear view of her necklace, I squinted through my lorgnette. She was wearing a miniature guillotine! I asked her name.

Looking up, her eyes beady, she replied, "Madame Defarge."

Impossible! What the dickens was she doing on my train?

"Is there something wrong with my name, monsieur?"

"N-no, of course not."

"And what is your name, *monsieur?*" she asked.

"Row . . . Row," I sputtered. Abruptly remembering my mission and my assumed identity, I answered, "*Inspecteur* Poirot, *madame,* at your service. Now, can you please tell me if anything unusual occurred here last night?"

She put aside her knitting and took the burned-down stogie out of her mouth. From her purse she pulled a new Havana. With a *click-clack-click* of her mini-guillotine, she cut off its tip. Puffing anew, she answered my question: "I heard all the screaming, but I was the only one to take action. I stabbed the raccoon with my knitting needle."

"*Oy, veh!.*" The 4:13 A.M. bash I had heard.

"Careful, my little *salami*. If you don't watch yourself, I'll cut you down to size," Madame said.

"What did you do then?"

"I nailed it to the back door of the caboose."

"Follow me, *Madame*," I said, walking toward the end of the train. My hair, it seemed, had taken on a life of its own. In the caboose, a group of passengers had gathered in a scene reminiscent of the *denouement* of an Agatha Christie mystery.

Our roommates were there, along with the aristocratic British couple, Was there a conspiracy? Were they all accomplices in the murder of my hair? I pushed through the crowd of suspects and then saw it — my hair, forlornly hanging impaled by a gold knitting needle. The erstwhile black hairs looked putrid and jaundiced. Upon closer inspection, the fine hairs were bashed in, rolled over, smashed and crushed. A few stood on end.

"*Alors, mes amis* [Then, my friends]," I said to the group, "*regardez*, how the droopy shape of the wild hair resembles a furry rodent." I peered intently through my lorgnette and nervously pulled out the long shiny needle. Then something happened that was as shocking as the climax of Agatha Christie's *Murder on the Orient Express*."

My beloved hair plummeted to the floor, and we all gazed with amazement as the hair slowly moved forward.

"*Oh la vache!* [Holy Cow!]" I screamed.

Click-Clack-Click. The seamstress of terror, who couldn't mend straight, clicked her guillotine.

"E-e-e-e-e-e!" one of the French girls screamed.

"Ohhhh!" came the collective sigh as the hair picked up speed.

"Stop that hair," I yelled, charging forward.

In desperation I hurled myself through the air like a football player, but my hair scampered away from my grasp. I had to have it, or I could not face the world again. I lunged once more and finally recovered my precious hair piece. I picked it up and to my complete horror recoiled in fright.

"*Oh mon dieu,*" I yelled.

"Oh, my Lord," gasped the English woman. Madame Defarge again pressed on her guillotine.

My beautifully curled moustache, quivering with fear, straightened into an arrow. There, before our eyes was the answer to the Affair of the Hair. A giant furry brown rat peeped his head out and disappeared to the rear of the caboose.

I thrust the corpse of my hair onto my head just in time as we pulled into the St. Lazare Station in Paris. Unkempt hair thrusting in every direction, I looked like the craziest of the Three Stooges.

Though I could never be as great a detective as Hercule Poirot, perhaps I was closer in intellect to Inspector Clouseau.

EPILOGUE

I have always wondered about the furry creature still haunting the corridors of the Paris Express. My advice to future night-train travelers: use caution. Put your hairpiece to bed in your suitcase before you go to sleep yourself. Unless a furry rat / rodent / raccoon steals your luggage, your toupée should be where you left it in the morning.

I never saw any of the passengers again. But I later learned that Madame Defarge was the great-great-great-great-granddaughter of the original. After clipping stogies for so many years, she realized she had a great talent for circumcision. Becoming one of the most celebrated mohels in the history of France, she introduced a new reign of terror to the republic. *Clickety-click-clack.*

Toupée or Not Toupée

That was the question when I first started losing my hair. My obsession with losing my hair reached its zenith when I entered the trauma of dating. When you're not a great lover with hair, how much can you expect without hair? I finally found the answer to my hairy obsession. I engaged in a great cover-up. I bought a toupée.

You may ask why I never mentioned my hairpiece before. Just as guys don't like to ask for directions, men don't want to talk abut losing their hair and replacing it with a rug. Being so shy, I couldn't reveal my secret before the affair of the hair. It was my big joke, my coming out party. Of course the joke was on me.

I looked over all kinds of hairpieces — real, synthetic, German, Swiss, Norwegian — even French pubic. Only one stood out, and that's the last one I got. *Vive La* France.

Wearing a toupée takes some getting used to. Every morning, when I stuck the hair on my head, I looked different, depending on the serendipity of where the hair landed. I first would place my hairpiece on my head as if I were landing a plane (of course, I had to make sure before the landing that no flies were on my hairodrome).

If my hair happened to land far down on my forehead, I could be mistaken for one of the Beatles. A little farther down and to the side, and with a beret on my head, I looked like Jean Paul Belmondo. Or, I could push my hair to the back of my head and be Mr. Cool Dude with a Convertible Cadillac.

In one of my more manic moods, I could place the rug on backwards on my head, and feel like Wrong-Way Corrigan. In a lecherous mood, I could put the hair at a rakish angle. Of course, if I wanted to have a real-me look, I could place the hairy piece sideways on my head, ear to ear, for the distinguished rodent look. The possibilities were endless.

Wearing a hat, I faced the grave danger of *losing* my hair every time I took my cap or hat *off*. Once the toupée stuck to the top of my hat, and I spent hours trying to find it. And wind! Oy! How I've always feared the sudden gusts that can blow the hair right off my head. One day I left work, and suddenly Olive Street Boulevard became a wind tunnel. My hair blew off despite the tape and pins I used to anchor it down. The toupée started scuttling down the street, and all I could do was chase after it, yelling, "Stop that hair! Stop that hair!" But the hairpiece was faster, scooting along, with helpful bystanders joining in the chase. A policeman whistled, cars screeched, women shrieked as the hairpiece dashed out into the intersection of Eighth and Olive. I watched with a broken heart as a transit bus ran it down.

Sad, crestfallen, and morose, I sat *shiva** for five nights with a *yarmulke* [little hat for prayer], covering my bald pate, mourning my beloved toupée.

---

* Sitting at home praying for the dead, from the Hebrew *shiva*, the Hebrew for seven.

The Odd Couple

As Juliet was to Romeo,
As Beatrice was to Dante,
As Mimi was to Rudolpho,
As Monica was to Bill,
So was my Sarah not to me.

As Katherine was to Petrouchio,
As Taylor was to Burton,
As Alice was to Ralph Cramden,
So did we bicker like the Bickersons.

But, at heart, we were closer to Felix Unger and Oscar Madison. We were "The Odd Couple."

Sarah and I were drawn together like the gravitational force between two heavenly bodies. She told me how much I needed someone to take care of me, look after me, clean up after me. "You're like a little boy who never grew up."

She was right. I was fighting several forces. The former was still in my mind, forcing me to repeat things. The latter was the law of gravity, which was my nemesis. I'd walk into the house at night, take off my coat, try to hang it up and it always fell immediately onto the floor. Whether a tie or a shirt, everything promptly plotzed. This was clearly not my fault. Blame it on Sir Isaac Newton.

"You know, I'm beginning to think that there's something wrong with you," she said.

"With me? What about you?"

"So, I'm color blind. I'm not a slob like you."

"I can't even drop a sock and expect it to fall on the floor before you grab it. It's not fair."

"I'm not talking about your stinking socks. You don't step on cracks, you check the locks five times, and you keep going back to check if the lights in your car are out."

"What about you worshiping your floors like they were made of gold? You're so clean you can't leave a dish in the sink for more than a minute," I said.

"What's wrong with practicing hygiene? I just like to be clean. It wouldn't hurt you to clean up your act. Why do you keep repeating things over and over?"

"I don't know. Why do you keep sweeping the floors?" I asked.

"You have nothing to complain about. Look how much money my clean house has saved you. We never use a maid!"

She noticed rituals that emerged. I tried to hide them from her, but as soon as I would cover up one, another would pop up.

"Why did you just push your glasses up with your nose?"

"I did? I never noticed."

"You just did it again," she said.

"I guess it's just a nervous tic. The market's been going down recently."

She commented on my checking and knocking on tables. I always found excuses, like making sure the house was secure and knocking on wood was a way of avoiding bad luck.

I continually manufactured believable reasons, but I wondered how long I would be able to come up with new fabrications before the well went dry. As much as I loved and trusted her I had this deep fear of revealing the awful truth. How could anyone possibly accept or understand this inner world of turmoil that I had hid for so long?

"Why can't you just stop it? Tell it to just go away. Why can't you tell yourself it's all nonsense?"

I remained silent, angry at her intolerance, but how could I blame her for not understanding?

She, like the rest of the world, was on the outside looking in, using everyday logic to understand my behavior. Someday, I would have to set the world straight.

Sarah came over to my side and held my hand. "I'll admit I may be excessively neat. It was the way I was brought up. But you always seem to be distant, as if you're in another world, thinking of something else, not to mention all these rituals you waste your time on. I think you should check yourself out with a doctor."

"You mean a psychiatrist?"

"Only if you wish, Honey," she said.

"Honey." The word stirred memories of my father, who always used that term of endearment after arguing with my mother.

I knew then she really loved me, and perhaps we weren't such an odd couple after all. The only thing I found odd was her suggesting I needed a psychiatrist. How could she? What was so strange about me? Doesn't everybody at some time have superstitions, knocking on wood, not stepping on cracks or walking under ladders, and never, never getting off on the thirteenth floor? How could she think such a thing? I knew she was going to say, "You're in complete denial."

No problem, I'll simply deny it.

Although I thought I had reached the peak of the commotion in my mind at the wedding, the mental storm was gathering force. Concentration became more difficult; reading was no longer enjoyable because I reread every line twice.

I had to fall back on fantasy, my favorite coping mechanism. I tried to shift my thoughts to more enjoyable places. So, my daydreaming would refocus me to a world beyond pain and reality and filled with humor.

Thus did a comet soar across the United States one evening. Startled, astronomers watched in horror as the fireball came down in the vicinity of St. Louis. Was this a catastrophic event about to happen? Of course not. It was merely Shleppriel coming in to cheer me up. My guardian angel simply mistook the stainless steel of the arch for the golden ones of McDonalds'. He was so hungry, he couldn't see straight, just like my wife.

THE ARCHANGEL
OF ST. LOUIS

During that night, Sarah and I were lying in bed playing Dueling Television Clickers as we vied for our favorite programs. We fenced like Shakespeare's Hamlet and Laertes. The television set went haywire as each of us made palpable hits, switching channels between the St. Louis Cardinals football game and *Sixty Minutes.*

Our clickers collided and Sarah's went flying across the room, leaving the Cardinal's game in view. We watched for ten minutes, then began making love. St. Louis was on the New York Giants' three-yard line. The fullback was hurling himself toward the end zone, when suddenly, the picture changed to a view of the brilliantly illuminated St. Louis Arch, atop which sat a large white, winged figure. We stopped to stare in amazement. At the foot of the north side of the arch a newscaster appeared.

"This is Tom O'Neal with Channel Two, reporting to you on a late-breaking news story. What appears to be a large figure with wings has slammed into the arch and is now sitting astride the apex. Eyewitnesses have reported they saw someone, or something, flying high from the east, then coming down in a straight line onto the arch. There appears to be no damage to the arch structure.

"He seems to have wings, or perhaps it's a hang-glider. He's moving. He's beginning to slide faster, faster. Here he comes," the TV reporter continued.

R-m-m-m-m-m-m-m. R-u-m-p.

"He's fallen on his rear end!"

R-i-p-p-p-p-p-p.

"It sounds like a rip in his pants. He's getting up. Mr. Angel, Mr. Angel. You are one, aren't you?" Mr. O'Neal asked.

The winged figure dusted himself off, dodging the mike. "How could I be an angel? Nobody believes in angels anymore," Shleppriel said.

"But the wings?"

"Oh, they're just a camouflaged hang-glider."

"But why did you come down on the arch?"

"Oh, I was just hungry, looking for a Big Mac burger, and thought I saw some arches that looked golden in the setting sun. They turned out to be silver."

"What is he, a comedian?" Sarah blurted out.

"No, he's Shleppriel."

"Who?"

"Oh, just a friend. You never know where he'll show up."

Tom O'Neal came on the television again. "The police have arrived and are taking the angel away."

"I haven't done anything wrong," he said.

The policeman interjected, "Trespassing on a public monument."

The angel pleaded, "But I'm innocent."

Mr. O'Neall intervened. "Mr. Angel, if you should happen to be one of those heavenly creatures, could you please give a message for us mortals?"

The angel looked up, smiled, and fluttered his wings. "Yeah, I know my rights. I want one phone call." He flapped his wings and produced the first celestial cell phone.

My phone rang. I picked it up quickly and said, "Hello."

"This is your guardian angel."

"Oh, Shleppriel, I was just watching you on television. What are you doing here?"

"I've come to help you. Listen, Shlep, you're falling off your ladder."

"What have I done?"

"You're arguing with your wife and not appreciating her. Do you have any idea what she's done for you?"

"No, I guess not."

"At some point, you'll realize how she's changed your life. Where would you be without her?"

His words pierced my heart. Hadn't I appreciated Sarah? Was I missing something in our relationship?

The television lit up again.

"This is Tom O'Neall again. The mayor has christened him, the 'Arch-angel of St. Louis.' And this just in: there's going to be a statue of him in front of Bush Stadium, right next to Stan Musial."

"Shlep, Shlep." My angel was back on the phone. "They're doing tests on me. I had a high *shmalz* reading, over two hundred-fifty, but it's okay, it's the good HDL *shmalz*. They want to do a biopsy on my wings. I've got to get out of here. But before I leave, I must give you my message. You want to be a *mensh*? Return to your spirituality."

"What has spirituality got to do with OCD?"

"Spirituality is the key to inner contentment."*

"How do I do that?" I asked.

"Do *mitzvot* [plural of *mitzvah*]. Reach out to people. *Mitzvot* mean all the commandments in the *Torah*. Get out of your head and help your fellow man. Devote your life to others and how to put the other person first. In this way you will not have time to obsess over yourself and find a new inner peace, called shalom.

"How many commandments are there?"

"Six hundred and thirteen."

---

* Inspired by Rabbi Abraham Twerski.

"That many?"

"Don't worry, nobody expects you to do them all. Besides, sixty are for women."

"Thank the Lord," I said as I slowly returned to my compulsive consciousness.

I returned to reality, though begrudgingly, for I was reluctant to let go of my Arch-angel. He kept my repetitive thoughts at bay. I was back in bed with my wife. The football game was still on and it was a complete bore: fumbles, interceptions, little action.

I turned to Sarah, thinking about what my angel had said about how I treated her. I realized I had difficulty expressing my love for her, a residue of the shyness of my youth. I embraced her with a new tenderness that would glow in the light of the television set.

THE MOAN

The football game was continuing and the St. Louis "Big Red" St. Louis Cardinals football team was driving down the field, when a dispute arose over whether the fullback fumbled before or after his knee hit the ground. We were curious as to the outcome of the game. The three referees congregated to look at the instant replay.* We waited and waited as minutes went by. What could we do; make love to Chopin's "Minute Waltz?"

"The Cardinals are calling for a replay."

"Oh, no," we said. "Another replay."

Suddenly, the game stopped and the chief referee, in a striped shirt, stepped forward, looking straight into the camera, and at us.

"Excuse me, folks, I don't mean to intrude, but we'd like to run an instant replay on you."

"He's got to be kidding, isn't he? Sarah asked.

"Oh, let him talk. This is interesting."

The referee continued. "This game is so boring, we prefer to watch your moves. And we could sure use a shot in our ratings."

"How could he ask us to do that?" Sarah asked.

"It's okay, it's okay," I said.

Fortunately, it was that time of the month when I was in heat, and I turned over in a passionate, falling, turning, twisting

---

* Although instant replay is an anachronism, I hope the reader will forgive my poetic license.

tsunami of love. After a tidal wave of passion, I thought I heard a mysterious sound.

"Sarah, you moaned, you moaned."

"I did?"

"I heard it."

"I don't think so."

"Let's ask the referee."

The referees conferred and then responded. "We're sorry, but it was clearly a loud burp."

We plunged in again.

"Ohhhhhh shhhh."

"I heard it. I heard it. I think she's got it."

"It's gas. No doubt about it," the refs chimed in.

I couldn't believe it. "Once more into the breach!" I yelled.

After thirty seconds I heard, "Oyyyyy veeeeeeh!"

The refs shouted with gleeful enthusiasm. "It's a moan!"

I knew she could do it. The first Jewish wife in history to moan.

"Mazel Tov," shouted one referee before signing off.

Unfortunately, I was hoping to be a "Shlong day's journey into night," but I was more like the war movie, *Thirty Seconds Over Tokyo.*

Of course, many of you will believe that "moan" was just another fantasy by that Walter Mitty shlepper. But that would not be completely right. Consider this, why would the Big Red football Cardinals, who only won four games that year, achieve a record 6.7 rating on the Nielsen that night? The audience certainly wasn't watching the boring game on the field.

A by-product of that wonderful moan was that nine months later our first lovely little girl was born. Her sister, another beauty, came into the world a year later.

A few months later, my wife's career soared. She announced, "I don't need your eyes anymore, I can succeed on my own," I was shocked, but everyone had to do their own thing and hers was a cockeyed view of wallpaper.

She decided to make her own cutting-edge, custom-colored wallpaper. She had her own vision of a dynamic, unexpected juxtaposition of clashing colors that kept the observer totally unbalanced.

At first, the startled public could only hold its breath, somewhat apoplectic. I never thought her bashing colors would sell. But, eventually, the "*oys*" turned into "ahs" and I heard a people calling her work of "a whirling dervish of technicolor reminiscent of Kandinsky." Finally, she got a feature in *St. Louis Homes and Lifestyles* magazine, calling her the "Jackson Pollack" of interior decorating.

I Hope I Get Cancer
Of the Fingernail

My father was growing older and more tired looking. Although he had stopped smoking for twenty years, my brother called and told me Pop had lung cancer. The doctor gave him six months to live. I rushed out the door, hearing Sarah in the distance, yelling, "Honey, where are you going?" Where? I had no idea. I just kept running, looking for the Hamilton Elementary schoolyard of my youth. But the schoolyard was at least twenty-six miles away and I was no marathon runner. Still I needed to stomp one hundred times again on that home plate of so many years ago. I knew the act had no effect on my grandmother and probably wouldn't help Pop now. But that made no difference to me.

A new intrusive thought stopped me cold: *I hope I get cancer of the fingernail, I hope I get cancer of the fingernail.*

The repetitions increased. *Cancer, fingernail, cancer, fingernail.* The thoughts had a life of their own, daring me to stop them. I tried to empty my mind, create a vacuum. *Nothing, nothing, nothing. One thousand-one, one thousand-two, five, ten, thirty, forty-five seconds.* I couldn't hold them back. *Cancer of the fingernail, I hope I get cancer of the fingernail.*

Why, why, why, I asked myself. Was I crazy? No, no. Did I really think my thoughts could keep Pop alive? Logically, no, but I had to think them.

Unlike the days when I counted all day at school, I was now pressing on a nail. Did I want to deflect the cancer from my father to my fingernail, which I could simply clip off? At last, some logic had entered my mind. Why did I repeat all this garbage, all the time? Was I more worried about my father, or myself? A cancerous fingernail could be cured, so I was ashamed of deflecting my anxieties into a mere fingernail. (Oh, Pop, how I loved you.)

These intrusive thoughts were not what I felt in my heart. I could not account for the way my mind worked. I had to stop the repetitious thoughts and rituals. Stop them, stomp them out of my brain. My ruminations about cancer of the fingernail alarmed me. Where was I heading? More phrases and more rituals? I was thirty-seven years old. Was I the only one with hellish thoughts? A light dawned in my brain. Was it remotely possible that I might have a mental disorder? Reluctantly, I had to admit the truth. Something was wrong.

✑

The next day, I asked my internist to recommend a psychiatrist. He mentioned a Doctor Rosen.

I called the number and heard a recorded voice. "The doctor is not in. To leave a message, please choose from the following options:

"If you have multiple personalities, press the number closest to the sum of the characters residing within you.

"If you hear voices, hang up and I will return your call. There is no need to remain by your phone.

"If you are obsessive, press seven fourteen times.

"If you have Tourette's Syndrome, fuck off."

This was the shrink for me.

I made an appointment. Dr. Rosen had a lean face, a wispy mustache that drooped at each end, tufts of graying eyebrows. First, the good doctor had me fill out a form about my life, education and profession. He read it through and asked, "What is disturbing you?"

"I've never been able to talk about it with anyone."

"Can you tell me about it?"

"I've been repeating phrases and acting out rituals since kindergarten," I said.

"Tell me about them."

"I can't. I'm so ashamed."

"Would you mind writing them down?"

"I think I can do that," I said.

He handed me a sheet of paper and a pen. For the first time in my life I wrote down all the damned thoughts I could remember:

Now I'm five, now I'm five.

Now I'm five, now I'm ten.

Flu, pneumonia.

It was so painful, I had to pause.

I hope I get cancer of the fingernail.

How stupid, I thought.

Hate God, love God.

I felt utterly embarrassed as I handed over the paper.

"Are these thoughts always with you?" he asked.

"Yes.

The doctor handed me a test with a hundred questions, which at the time was a standard test for OCD. The questions seemed all too familiar:

Do you have fears of contracting illnesses?

Do you keep repeating certain phrases in your mind?

Do you check and recheck the same thing, like locks and lights?

Do you have certain lucky numbers that you repeat?

Do you reread sentences?

When you finish a test before the time limit, do you keep going over the questions until the last second?

Have you ever tapped things continually?

How did they know me so well? The next question absolutely

chilled me: Did you ever look at a knife and want to pick it up and use it on someone?

How could anyone know my darkest secret?

The doctor kept asking me if I had finished the test. He must have known I had to recheck every question.

"Give me the test already. You think you're back in college again?" he demanded. Reluctantly, I relinquished the papers.

After ten minutes he announced, "I've got good news and bad news."

"Give me the bad news first."

"The bad news is that you've got a severe case of Obsessive Compulsive Disorder."

"What's the good news?"

"You scored a hundred."

I had to work my nuts off to get a B-plus average in college and here I ace a test with a hundred.

He explained Obsessive Compulsive Disorder as: Repetitive, intrusive thoughts or rituals associated with significant levels of anxiety. "Both the thoughts and the rituals are very difficult to resist or stop. Resistance can generate further anxiety," he said. "This condition usually starts during childhood or adolescence. It is a chemical imbalance that causes your brain to misfire. First there is the obsessive thought, which causes anxiety, and then a compulsive ritual, like hand washing or light checking to control or reduce the anxiety. Other symptoms are depression and anxiety."

I told the doctor how I stomped my feet a hundred times in the schoolyard, hoping to extend my grandmother's life.

"That's OCD."

"It is?"

"Of course, the very essence. The thought of your grandmother dying was something you could not deal with. It caused great anxiety and you sought refuge in the counting ritual, with each number representing another year of her life. Counting eased your anxieties and, in turn, resulted in 'Magical Thinking,' the feeling that a miracle would occur. But of course it didn't."

"If a person checks a lock at night, and then goes back and checks again, does he have OCD?"

"No, only when he absolutely knows the locks are secure and he still has to go back time after time to check them. That's OCD and why the French call it the doubting disease.

"Can I be cured?"

"To be honest, no. We don't have a cure yet."

"What can I do?"

"Try to turn your obsessive thoughts into something positive. What did you study in college?"

"English."

"So, write a book. Write what you know. Instead of obsessing over one thing after another, pour your thoughts into writing. Turn this malicious obsession into a magnificent obsession."

I thanked the doctor for his advice and the drug Imimpramine. He told me he understood my case because he suffered from depression himself. He had once spent a week in the hospital, unable to rise from his bed. Although that bothered me at the time, I could not image that his story would someday come back to haunt me.

I had always wanted to write. First, I tried journalism, but couldn't write fast enough to make the deadlines. Desperate, I switched to writing fiction, but alas, I could never create a memorable character. That is, until now. At last, I had found a character so appealing, so huggable, and so obviously lovable — me. Then I discovered, as in a novel, I had a protagonist — me, like Don Quixote — a confidante, like Sancho Panza, who was Shleppriel, my guardian angel, and an antagonist far worse than a windmill — the OCDemon.

I would write my memoir, not only looking back on thirty-seven years of struggle, but also looking forward to change the future — a living memoir. I had reached, as Dante said in his *Inferno*, "The midway upon the journey of our life, I found myself in a dark wood where the right way was lost." But I would never descend into the limbo of hell. Somehow, I would ascend my ladder.

Thus began my writing career. On a Saturday afternoon in 1969 I sat down in my living room and flipped on KFUO radio. I listened to the Texaco Metropolitan Opera broadcast for the first time. In some mysterious manner my creative powers tuned into the sublime music of Mozart, Puccini and Verdi. For the next thirty years I would write and rewrite and rewrite in the best traditions of an OCDer. After all this time, I had little to show for it but became an expert on opera without ever studying a note. After the broadcast I found myself whistling arias.

My heart soared when I head the beautiful aria from "Don Giovanni," "*La ci darem la mano*" (Lay your hand in mine, dear). The tender duet between Don Giovanni and Zerlina kept coming into my mind when obsessive thoughts were hammering my consciousness. In response I whistled the music and found a greater serenity than I had known from my show tunes.

DISTINGUISHED COMPANY:
JOE DIMAGGIO, MARCEL PROUST,
HOWARD HUGHES, AND ME

֍

At the library I looked up everything possible about OCD and discovered that many famous sufferers had preceded me: Lady Macbeth incessantly washing her bloody hands, Captain Ahab with his O Sea D, Estragon and Vladimir waiting, waiting, waiting for Godot, Humbert Humbert obsessing over Lolita, Javert devoting his life to chasing Jean Valjeans in *Les Miserables*, and Captain Queeg of *The Caine Mutiny* passionately playing with his balls. The most surprising celebrity turned out to be Joe DiMaggio, who was so obsessively neat he kept everything alphabetized. A-Aspirin, B-book, C-comb, and at the end of the night table, X-Xanax.

I also came across the French writer Marcel Proust, a fellow Jew, who strangely reminded me of me. He spent over twenty years writing and rewriting his magnum opus "In Search of Lost Time." Frustrated with the delays, his publisher demanded the final manuscript. Proust reluctantly complied, then tried rewriting, instead of proofreading, the galleys. It didn't take a genius to see that the poor fellow had OCD. I feared that I, too, would pour my quest for perfection into my memoir. I would ultimately beat Proust's record, rewriting my mini-opus thirty-two times, the epitome of OCD.

I ran across a *Life* magazine article featuring one of the most daring airplane pilots, who also happened to be an entrepreneur, film maker, bon vivant, and one of the great Hollywood ladies man of the forties. He had millions of dollars, power, celebrity and all the trappings of success. He could do everything but fight off his horrific fear of germs that plagued him all his life. His name was Howard Hughes.

He had become a recluse by 1969, hiding from the one fear he could not overcome or buy his way out of. I looked deeper in the library files. How could anyone fly around the world in 1938, after an earlier crash, and show no fear? But now the man with the world's largest flying machine was hiding from his abhorrent germs. From my research, I knew he was an OCDer. He had to have it. So I began following every mention of him in the newspapers. Reports surfaced that his uncut nails grew wildly, hanging like claws, that his hair grew wildly, aging him like Methuselah. Evidently, his OCD had run amuck, and the obsessive demon was controlling him. A chilling thought intruded on me: Would I experience the same thing?

Behavior exposure and response therapy were not in widespread use when I began my struggle. I had no choice but to use the trial and error method. I would try anything if it worked.

Choosing what I considered the easiest ritual to conquer, not stepping on cracks, I took a walk and surveyed the cracks on the sidewalks. Like a little boy dipping his toe in a cold swimming pool, I forced myself to touch the tip of a crack with the toe of my shoe. When I looked around, the sun was still shining in the warm blue skies. Yee God, nothing had happened. I tried again and still no lightning struck. I touched my toe to the crack every day for a week and gradually moved my shoe further onto the crack. Summoning all my courage and stomping forcefully on the crack, I yelled, "Out, out, damn crack." I stomped again, for the first time perceiving that no ritual can change anything.

When I attacked my need to reread sentences and knock on desks and tables, I feared something dreadful would happen, even though I knew otherwise. Slow, always slow, don't reread it. Don't knock on wood. Every time I avoided the rituals, I felt my neurons shaking, trembling, pressing, pressing against my skull. *I will defeat the OCDemon.* I repeated it. As a ritual surfaced, I revolted. Out, out, damn thought. Get out of my mind. Why are you intruding on my privacy? *Check the lights, check the lights.* No way, no way. I felt the pressure mounting, mounting. Stop, stop, stop. I grimaced as I brought to bear all my powers of concentration. The force of anxiety was rising like a wave in physics. If I could just hold on until the peak passed. I squeezed my eyes shut and slowly felt the wave ebbing.

I learned that anxious thoughts cannot crest indefinitely. They only reached full strength for a matter of seconds. If I could somehow manage not to react, the thoughts might lose their power over time. To fight the ritual of checking the lights, I created another ritual, saying to myself:

I turned the lights off.

I turned the lights off.

I turned the lights off.

For months, I battled, sometimes unsuccessfully, the urge to go back and check. Finally, I drew up the courage, like the lion in the *Wizard of Oz*, to stop doubting myself. I vowed never to check the lights again.

That evening I felt I had won the first skirmish. I casually walked to my car full of pride. But wide-eyed in shock, I saw the lights were on.

I could hear the demon laughing from the remote corners of my brain. He had won the first skirmish, but I knew I would win the battle because I no longer cared whether the lights were on or off. Better the lights be on than perform another checking ritual.

I wondered why I had made progress fighting OCD, but Howard Hughes had met with defeat. All that money and he still succumbed. But maybe money was his problem. His wealth was an enabler, allowing him to remake the world around him to accommodate his OCD, allowing it to flourish and gain ultimate control. Perhaps with no urgency to seek help, and no need to fight, his financial security blanket could kill him.

POP AND HOWARD

My father passed away on April 5, 1976. The *St. Louis Globe Democrat* gave my father a write-up on the obituary page with his picture. In his later years, he worked as an executive secretary of Temple Israel. Everyone loved him because he did little things that meant a lot, like tape recording the *Bar Mitzvahs* as a surprise for the parents. He was kind to people who couldn't afford the dues to join the congregation. He let them pay whatever and whenever they could. All the members of the congregation considered him a *mensh*.

Next to my father's obituary in the paper was another, with a photo that startled me: Howard Hughes.

How could there be such a coincidence, two people of such opposite natures dying on the same day? Here was Pop, who was always ascending his ladder, pictured close to Howard Hughes, who was obviously descending into the abyss of OCD! Was someone up high telling me something?

After Pop passed away, I received telephone calls all day from people I never knew before, expressing their sympathy. I heard stories about Pop that I had never heard before:

"Your father, Mike, was one of a kind. If it hadn't been for him, we couldn't have joined the Temple. He reduced the dues so we could afford to join."

"He was the kindest man. He let us pay off our dues in installments so our boy could go to Sunday School and get *Bar Mitzvahed*. He never wanted us to say a word."

"We were so grateful he recorded our son's *Bar Mitzvah*. He never even asked for our or the Temple's permission. He just told us to keep it quiet."

"He sold us some mutual funds in 1931, and I never thanked him since they went up to a million dollars."

The accolades came in for the next few days, but Pop had always told them not to mention what he had done for them. Who knew? How could I know? Not until after my father's death did I fully realize what a *mensh* he was.

∽

I compared my father's life with that of Howard Hughes. Although Hughes had all the power and money, his was a wasted life. He was one of the worst examples of falling under the spell of OCD, imprisoned by his illness, dying a horrible, filthy and degrading death. There was nothing about Howard Hughes, especially his OCD, I wished to emulate. It was my father to whom I wished to turn to as a role model.

The doctor prescribed Anafranil for me. Much to my surprise I noticed a difference, but not a cure, within two weeks. The repetitive thoughts faded a bit, as did the pressure on my mind.

Then the unthinkable happened. My *shmeckel* dropped dead.

As each day went by, I grew more obsessed with my impotence.

I returned to the doctor and told him I felt some improvement with the drug. His eyes glowed with excitement as he pounded his fist on the desk. "Now we're getting somewhere," he said.

"But," I interrupted, "my libido is dead as a mackerel."

"Hmm." He paused. "I did say there were side effects."

"I don't remember you mentioning that one."

"Wouldn't you rather be less bothered by OCD than have sex?"

I paused, like Jack Benny pondering the question, "Your money or your life?"

"Hell no," I yelled, throwing the pills on the desk. "Screw the OCD. I can somehow overcome it on my own. Give me sex. I can't live without it."

∽©∼

I started thinking about Wink and his nudist colony in France. It may, indeed, be time for me to crawl out of my shell on a beach. After all, it would be the ultimate fantasy come true for a person like me. I also thought that at last I had a chance to shake off the *shlepper* shackles and the messy clothes. How could I get mustard, ketchup, and salad stains on my clothes if I didn't wear any?

I had to ask my wife what she thought of my idea. All she could do was laugh.

"Oh, my little Walter Mitty, you certainly are the biggest daydreamer since Don Quixote. You think I'm going to take off all my clothes in front of all those *goyim*?"

"They won't care."

"But I will. Go by yourself. I can't leave my soaring career now. But I doubt you'll find what you're looking for. The problem is you have to take your head with you."

"I'm going to deshlepperize myself."

My Bon Voyage to a Nudist Colony

𝒶

I did some research at the library and found the world's largest nudist colony at Cap D'Agde, France. I flew to Paris, took the train to Lyon, and on to my great adventure.

"I'M IN THE NUDE FOR LOVE"

❦

Voila! C'est moi! Thousands of French eyes would be looking only at me. I had come to Cap D'Agde, the world's largest nudist beach, located on France's Mediterranean coast about one hundred-fifty miles due west of Marseille.

Some of my customers couldn't understand why I, being so shy, would ever go. All they had ever gone to was a fantasy baseball camp. But playing with fully dressed professionals on a baseball diamond simply couldn't compare.

Le Quartier Naturist was a large, modern resort with three six-story crescent-shaped condominiums, about ten restaurants, swimming pools, tennis courts, lingerie shops, a bank, and a filling station. Other than the resort's employees, everyone else could go nude. One area, called the Heliopolis, was home to a pharmacy, variety store, grocery store, bar, and several restaurants.

The first day I decided to move slowly, to acclimate myself and figure out how to dress, or undress, without distress. I put on my black socks, a white T-shirt, and tennis shorts.

Hungry, I stopped at "Delices d'Alsace" restaurant for *le petit dejeuner* (breakfast) and watch the passing parade. Two nude young girls sat at a nearby table. This was indeed a *g-ass*-tronomical restaurant for watching heavenly bodies.

After a delicious breakfast of croissants, crepes, and *une baguette* with great coffee, I sauntered over to the grocery store. Imagine everyone in the nude, pushing a shopping cart or "chariot." How did people carry money? Either in their hands, a little purse, or a money belt. (Other options were unthinkable.)

A fetching brunette with a Brigitte Bardot smile and a cute

little rear end walked in holding a miniature French poodle to her bosom. She either adored her pet (as most French do) or she felt somewhat shy about fully exposing her breasts (as most French don't). "Follow that *derrierè*," I commanded myself as I pursued her with my chariot. After she selected some brie, chardonnay, and apples, her dog began to squirm and yelp. "*Arrète! Arrète!*" she scolded, stop already. With a mighty bark, the dog jumped, using her bosom as a launching pad and landing on the eggplants. "*Arrète!*" she screamed again, dashing after her pet. I should be such a lucky dog.

Outside, walking with many nude couples past the rows of beige condominiums along the main road, I reached the beach. I couldn't feel the sand because I still wore my tennis shoes and socks. The bright glare of the Mediterranean Sea, presided over a vast expanse of beach, a rainbow of yellow, blue, green and red parasols. Beneath their shade some of the nudists reclined, slept or read. Others walked by the water or played paddleball in the sea. I bought my own pink parasol. Sticking its sharp end into the sand, I grabbed a stone, as I was instructed, pounded the pole downward.

I laid back on a towel, inhaling the moist sea air. Many of the girls who passed seemed to have materialized from the centerfolds of *Playboy* and *Penthouse* magazines. Had I entered Heaven's Gate? Not quite, as a number of specimens from *Modern Maturity* reminded me.

Still, I was an outsider, for I had yet to disrobe. Summoning the courage to take off my shoes was like calling a girl. I procrastinated and watched some girls playing volleyball, a great juggling act of balls and boobs.

Only the sight of the men, their dangling batons bouncing as they walked to the rhythm of the Mediterranean waves, revolted me. The males showed their age, presumably the bigger the pear-shape belly, the older the guy.

The time had come for my own unveiling. I was ready to make my own fashion statement and sensed a great hush of expectation on the beach. I stood up in the midday sun and, just like Gypsy Rose Lee tantalizing her audience, I slowly took off my socks and then my T-shirt. I was sure thousands of French eyes were staring at me. I inched my shorts down my hips, then let them drop in the sand. My alabaster skin gleamed in the sun. I felt like I had eaten the apple from the Garden of Eden. I felt like Adam after eating the forbidden fruit and felt his shame at his nakedness. I imagined his fig leaf on me. I even imagined myself as Michelangelo's David, but without so much as a slingshot. Looking at the sky, my arms stretched upwards, I felt like shouting: "*Liberté, Fraternité, Egalité.*"

I had joined the fraternity of nudists, free from the shackles of society. Surprisingly, I didn't feel embarrassed. When everyone is nude, it feels perfectly normal to bare one's soul. But I had to draw the line somewhere. I refused to take off my toupée.

Five yards away, six giggly, young French girls, obviously flush with lust, rushed toward me. Though I extended arms to embrace them, they sailed past and joined three young French hunks.

In hopes of making someone's acquaintance I walked along the beach. Although *La Plage Naturiste* was the most open place in the world, it remained at the same time very private. Taking photos was strictly prohibited. Random introductions felt out of place, too. You couldn't just go up to a beautifully bronzed woman, sitting there with her bosom hanging out, her eyes looking skyward, and say, "*Shalom.* I'm a shlepper from America." Nudism can be a barrier, a fence, but with no looking between the slats.

During my stroll I overheard a middle-aged couple speaking English. They turned out to be Londoners, who had been coming to Cap D'Agde every summer for fifteen years.

"Ah, we love it here," the wife told me. "You know, living in England, we don't see much sun. We rent a condominium in Agde for the month of August and soak up as much as we can."

"What do your friends and relatives think of your summer vacation?" I asked.

"Oh, no, no. We'd never tell anybody about this place," the husband said. "They'd be shocked. The English are too reserved for this kind of thing."

The English really do go to a nude beach just for the sun, I concluded.

I saw no evidence of overt sexuality, no visible erections on the beach at day. Could it be that amid an embarrassment of riches, the central nervous system, in charge of sexuality, simply gets overwhelmed and short-circuits the sensual light bulb.

When nothing is left to the imagination, the libido may lose its charge. The best example occurred when a slender flat-chested woman passed me with a plain face and no figure. (Her waist as wide as her hips.) That evening, when I saw the same girl walking with her boyfriend, I almost didn't recognize her. She wore red lipstick, make-up, a tight white plastic dress with a tight black belt, and extra high, high-heeled shoes. Her breasts were pushed up like a *Playboy* bunny's and she walked with a sexy sway. I couldn't believe it. The nude girl who did nothing to me in the afternoon was giving me a charge fully dressed. *Oy*, veh, I came all the way to Cap d' Agde to fulfill a lifetime fantasy about girls, only to discover they looked better with their clothes on.

At night the guys wore shorts or slacks with sport shirts. Some women paired shorts with blouses that often exposed sexy lingerie. Others wore leather outfits. But surprisingly, a number of women went topless.

The next morning I exited my apartment *tout nu*, confident, defiant and with no sense of embarrassment. I had now become part of the ambiance.

At the beach I spent several hours under my parasol, inter-rupted only by a sweet voice singing:

"*Beignets, glace . . . fraise.*"
It was a young girl, wearing a light dress and a bandana in her hair, and chanting: "Doughnuts, ice cream, strawberries." The sun had given me a ravenous appetite. I went over to my favorite restaurant, "The Horizon."

I ordered *une* salad, *un* hamburger, *un* spaghetti *avec* meatballs, *des pommes frites, et* some ice water. I tasted the delicious lettuce leaves and felt something cold on my chest. A glob of salad dressing sat nonchalantly on my left nipple. Undaunted, I bit into *le* hamburger and noticed a squirt of ketchup land on my bellybutton. Too hungry to be bothered, I plunged into my spaghetti and meatballs. The first meatball never got to my mouth. It fell off my fork, bounced off my stomach, and lodged between my other two balls, making me feel like the owner of a pawnshop. That was enough. Preparing to scrub myself clean, I dunked my napkin into the ice water, but accidentally knocked over the glass, spilling the ice onto my lap, and putting my crown jewels into a deep freeze. B-r-r-r! Where were my clothes when I needed them?

But who needs clothes in such a place? Wrong. Can you guess what's done for entertainment at a nudist colony? People watch a fashion show!

The best show took place at the "Waikiki Restaurant." The tables were arranged around an open pool, and a master of ceremonies presented four beautiful French models, who were also disco champions.

That evening, I returned to the Horizon Restaurant, which sits on a hillside overlooking the beach. As the sun set I felt a gentle breeze blowing in from the golden waters of the Mediterranean.

I felt exhilarated, joyful to be alive. A French *chanteur* was singing old American popular songs, like Pat Boone's, rendering of "Love Letters in the Sand."

I closed my eyes and bit into one of the specialties of the house, *moules frites* (mussels with French fries). The flavorful little crustaceans tickled my taste buds. I looked around at the view, the other couples enjoying themselves, the ambience, and the music, and finally understood what was meant by French *joie de vivre*.

After dinner, I checked out a store called "Doris D's." It was a strange name, but then it dawned on me. In French the letter "A" is pronounced "Ah," "B" is pronounced "Bay," "C" is "say," and "D" is "Day, so the store was pronounced "Doris D'ays." I'm sure the actress would have been honored to know that. Right under the neon sign I noticed the store's motto: "Brevity is the soul of lingerie." (Note: Doris D's has since been closed. The current spot is called the "Metamorphoses.")

I was taking notes in a notepad and had just written the name down. A lady from the shop came up and asked:

"What are you doing, *monsieur*?"

"I'm writing a memoir and Cap D'Agde is one of the climactic chapters. What is your name? I'll immortalize you."

"My name is Nadia."

I walked in the shop and Nadia showed me a mannequin wearing a matching black leather bra and panties set.

"You like, monsieur?" she asked.

"Well, they are pretty."

"Are you married?"

"Yes."

"Your wife would just love it."

"You don't know my wife," I said.

"Ah, but I do know women," Nadia said. "And they love the feel of leather. It oozes with sexual excitement. Look how pretty that young girl over there looks trying them on."

I looked over to the dressing room, but how could there be any in this place? Just dressing-up areas. I spotted the same girl who had done nothing for me undressed at 4 PM, had given me a charged dressed at 7 PM, and now she was absolutely devastating at 10 PM semi-dressed in leather.

"I'll take the set," I said. I would have a present to bring home to Sarah.

"*Merci, monsieur.*"

Au revoir, madame."

After leaving the store I wandered back to the square where I saw some of the sexily clad couples walking toward a place I hadn't noticed before, a nightclub called "Direction Le Paradiso." Couples were lined up, hand in hand, so I figured I could join the party. As I neared the entrance, I saw the sign, "Couples Only."

"No, no, *monsieur*, you cannot enter. It's for couples only," the man said.

"What have you got against me?"

"*Je regrette, monsieur*, you are not allowed in."

Why? Why? I wondered. Could this be some kind of discrimination? Maybe they were saying, *shleppers* are not welcome. How could they know? They couldn't tell by my dress. I rushed back to Nadia and asked why I couldn't go in.

"No, *monsieur*," she said, "only couples who like, as you say, to swap partners."

"Oh, my God. That is not my cup of wine."

"It's called *une boite de nuit échangiste*, a nightclub for swapping partners. We do a lot of business from them. Once your wife tries on her new outfit, maybe she would like to come join in."

What a ridiculous thought. I was on a different planet and it dawned on me that these people came here for many reasons.

For most families, it was the beach, a healthy way of life. Some women expected to reassert their attractiveness, and I'm sure many guys went to reawaken their libido. And, of course, there was that small percentage who believed in partner swapping. As for me, I had completed a great voyage of discovery. I had learned a lot, but alas, you can take the clothes out of the *shlepper*, but you can't take the *shlepper* out of the man.

♪♪

Bonjour, Sarah. I had arrived at Cap D'Agde in the nude for love and was coming home in the mood *pour l'amour*. I had completed my journey, and like Ulysses, a.k.a. Leopold Bloom, I returned to my Penelope, in other words, my Sarah. I was no longer an ill *Yid*, but a horny Jew.

On the plane home a strange feeling of loneliness came over me. Here I had been in a place most men fantasize about, but I simply didn't fit in. I was lonely for my wife and had to show her I cared.

As I approached the door the thought occurred to me, the only possible thing I could say. I opened the door and yelled, "Hello, Honey, I'm home." She ran and embraced me.

"I can't believe you actually called me Honey. Are you sure there's nothing wrong?"

"No, no, I have something for you, honey."

"For me? How thoughtful," she said.

I nervously awaited her reaction. I was afraid to look.

"Oh, you shouldn't have."

"The saleslady told me you'd love it."

Sarah eagerly tore open the wrapped paper and spied the two-piece outfit. She paused, then slowly said, "What is . . .? What is this? A . . . a . . . ?"

"A bra and panty set," I said.

"A *what?*" she asked, her eyes bulging.

"Yes, and they're all expensive leather."

She felt deep into the leather, rubbing her fingers. I cringed, waiting for some scream. All I heard was, "Oh, ohhh, o-h-h-h-h-h-h-h. I *love* leather."

"You do?"

"I crave it. That's why I bought all those shoes and purses."

"You have a fetish."

"Yes, yes, yes."

"Why didn't you tell me?"

"I was afraid you'd think I was crazy," she said. "The same reason you didn't tell me about your OCD."

"You know about my OCD? How could you possibly know?"

"Well, I always knew there was something not kosher with you. But then I saw someone just like you on my favorite TV talk show, *Oprah*. She threw her arms around me and said, "I love your present. It puts me in the mood for love."

"I can't believe it! Both of us at the same time! Oh, my teeny weenie. It's going to be so wonderful."

It was a wonderful and revolutionary evening. I set a personal record worthy of Don Juan. I was no longer "Thirty Seconds Over Tokyo," I was a "Minute Man."

I felt I was in control of my thoughts and had made great progress. I had made an appointment with my psychiatrist, eager to tell him about my latest adventures at the nudist colony. I figured he could always use a laugh and my stories would be just the right pick-me-up. But it would be no laughing matter.

I called the nurse and asked for an appointment.

"I'm sorry," she said, "the doctor is not making appointments."

"Is he on vacation?"

"You might say that."

"Then why can't I make an appointment?"

"He's not seeing patients any more."

"What do you mean? He always sees me," I said.

"I'm sorry, Mr. Fadem, I'm only doing my job." She hung up.

How could he not want to see me? I picked up the phone. The receptionist answered.

"I have to know, I have to know," I said.

"The doctor was in the hospital for a month with depression and he checked himself out last night and shot himself."

WHEN YOUR PSYCHIATRIST COMMITS SUICIDE, YOU KNOW YOU'RE IN DEEP DOO DOO

❧

I suppose while the doctor was giving me Xanax, I should have been giving him my Prozac. When I told people what happened, they laughed and said things like, "You've got to be kidding. I've never heard of such a thing. He really did it? Oh, that's terrible." Then the tragedy sunk in.

And so it was with me. Weak jokes proved no shield against my deepening abyss of anxiety and despair. I was traveling through a neurological storm, my ritualistic thoughts running amok.

Flu,pneumoniahateGodloveGodIhopeIdon'tgetcancerofthe fingernailfluflufluflukissofdeathkissoflifekissofdeathkissoflife sevensevensevensixfivefourfourfourfourcancerofthefingernail fingernailhateGodloveGodkissofdeathkissoflifeIhopeIdon'tget IhopeIdon'tgetaIhopeIdon'tIhopenowI'mfivenowI'mten seventhheavenseventhheavenIhopeIdon'tgetIdon'tgetacancer IhopeIdon'tgetacancer.

I tried in vain to slow the compulsion. S-l-o-w. Slow. I summoned up the strength to combat this irrational, magical curse in my mind. The gray cells of my cerebrum refused to enter a state of suspended animation. My head was a pressure cooker, waiting, waiting to explode.

Finally, this demon in my brain poured out, like a gargoyle down spout from Notre Dame Cathedral spewing out its guts on a dark stormy day. I shouted for all the world to hear:

"NOWI'MFIVENOWI'MTENKISSOFDEATHKISSOFLIFE ONETWOTHREEFOURTHREETWOONEHATEGodLOVE

God CANCERFINGERNAIL .... Damn you, damn you bastard fiend. Get out of my mind. There must be a way to rid myself of this devil, the son of a bitch."

Crazed with fear, I stumbled back into the house. I felt as if I were losing control. Here, for the past year, I thought I was winning the battle against my obsessions. Had my nemesis merely been hiding like a cancer in remission, waiting to pounce?

My eyes froze on the object that had startled me in childhood. The one thing I could not bear, a knife on the counter. *Pick it up, pick it up,* came the thought. *Pick it up, pick it up.* I couldn't block the thought. *Pick it up. Hurt someone.* I grabbed the knife, holding on with all my strength.

Drawn into the vortex of the OCDemon, I felt dizzy, my hands clammy, my heart palpitating as I found myself falling, falling into the darkness of my hellish whirlpool. I tried to fight with all the magical forces I had always relied on: willpower, humor, fantasy. All were beyond my reach. For the first time, I felt hopeless, desperate, hellbent to crawl out of my skin.

At the nadir of my life, I could see no way to rise. I attempted to drop the knife, drop the knife, but I froze. I couldn't let go. The blade flashed in the darkness, ghoulishly illuminating a latent memory. My mother was cutting the chocolate cake with that knife, the one that filled me with horror. I felt the same searing pain that had accompanied my first intrusive thought of hurting someone. No, no, no. The sweet morsel of chocolate, the dastardly blade.

Its gleam pierced my eyes, scorched my soul. More memories. More terror. My hands trembled, my throat tightened. Anything would be better than coping with my pain. "Oh, God," I begged. Where was the angel of the Lord who told Abraham to put down the knife on the altar with Issac? Where was a sign?

I paused and then I raised the knife.

BRAMMMMMM!

৯

A hot air balloon came crashing through my living room window with Shleppriel hanging onto the basket. Shards of glass went flying, as did the knife in my hand.

I woke up. "Shleppriel, you're here," I cried.

"I felt your pain," he said, "and flew faster than a jet before I crashed into a couple of hot air balloons, some kind of Forest Park Balloon Race you have every year. I tried to dodge them, but there were so many, I got entangled with a beautiful red, blue, and green one. Then we headed straight for your house. Sorry about all this, but something had to shock you back to your senses. You weren't going to stab anyone, including yourself."

"How do you know?"

"Because you are a caring person. Besides, OCD people like you don't act on such impulses. That would be psychotic and you are not that. Why do you think you feel so guilty when heinous thoughts hammer you? Because you care. If you didn't, they wouldn't bother you, and cause all the guilt and anxiety. That is the difference between you and a homicidal maniac, who acts on his malicious thoughts." With that, Shleppriel picked his way though the glass and disappeared.

I finally recognized that I had an evil twin in my soul, the dark twin of OCD: one rational, the other absurd. How could someone like me, whom I honestly felt to be of above-average intelligence, allow himself to do seemingly senseless things? Why couldn't the normal, healthy part of my mind destroy the senseless part? It was like Steven King's character in *The Dark*

Half, who had an evil twin in his soul. Could I have a dark twin of OCD, bent on destroying the good half?

I realized I reveled in nostalgia. The past is a friendly country — so reliable, so safe and secure. You have such freedom to remember the "good old days" and neglect the bad ones.

As I flipped through the pages of my memoir I saw the fading family photographs. Some made me smile, some left me sad as I gazed on my parents looking out at me. Both were gone, but I could feel their pride in me.

Rereading these passages was like an awakening of the mind. I realized I could not cure OCD, I could only learn to cope, and contain it. I could not kill this devil because it was a glitch in the brain. I could not stop these repetitive thoughts; I could only learn not to react to them.

Go ahead, damn thoughts, all you want. I found a niche in my brain for the glitch. I decided to imagine a section of my head where I drew a circle with my finger. Let the thoughts congregate and dance around all they wanted and enjoy each other's company. Just leave me alone. Someday I would find a way to cut, with the sharpened blades of a scissors, the maniacal tentacles of the OCDemon.

WHAT IF?

Variations of the same question recur frequently to me:
What if...

- *I was right that the world was too scary for me to come out of the womb?*
- *I pick up a knife and use it on someone?*
- *I don't knock on wood and something terrible happens?*
- *I don't check the locks and someone burglarized my house?*
- *I don't say "Love God, love God, love God" and He sought vengeance on me?*
- *I don't perform in bed or on my job and I felt humiliated?*

Each time, the question is followed by a quickening heartbeat, and a heavy feeling in my chest.

Why don't I say "What if I win the lottery today?" Or, "What if I have a record sales day?" No, only the negative outcomes emerged, proving the old OCD adage of being the doubting disease.

So-called "normal" people may have "What if?" but they can quickly refocus. The OCD sufferer keeps obsessing. I heard somewhere that we are governed by our thoughts, which become our reality. What if I could give my negative thoughts a positive spin? Then perhaps I could calm my hasty heart.

A KEY TO WINNING

"Do not go gentle into that good night.
Rage, rage against the dying of the light."
—Dylan Thomas

Is there a key for winning the battle against a mental disorder? You have two choices: give in like Howard Hughes and go down the drain. Or fight, fight, fight.

The OCDemon is a terroist at large in your mind. Its goal is to destroy your life. Therefore, declare war on Al Qaeda of your mind. Every day, wake up ready to do battle. Why do some OCD sufferers make great strides and others not respond? Because they haven't acquired the mindset of a victor. To win battles you must conquer your mind.

EVEN STEVEN

❧

My new psychiatrist, Dr. Benjamin Levin, an Orthodox Jew, came highly recommended for his treatment of Orthodox Jews with OCD. I had met him at a fundraiser. He had a thick, curly, black beard and large thick glasses riding on the bridge of his ample nose. During our first session, he said something that shocked me: "A disproportionate number of Orthodox Jews suffer from OCD.

I asked whether my OCD had roots in my Orthodox upbringing.

"Perhaps, but it's more likely in the genes. But a strict, ritualistic religion may bring out a predisposition for OCD. Catholics have the same problem.

A trauma in your life may bring out the disorder. It doesn't have to be major like the loss of a spouse, but rather things like entering adolescence or changing jobs or schools.

"The recurring image of the knife continues to terrify me."

That trauma worsened your condition, but at the heart of OCD is a disconnect between thought and reality. The intrusive, unwarranted thought creates a hoax on you. The thought creates a horrible feeling of wanting to hurt someone. But that OCD mind is fooled into accepting the idea as fact, when it is the opposite of reality."

I asked him about the blasphemous thoughts, *Hate God, hate God.*

"You feel like you're sinning? Creating a blasphemy?"

"Yes."

"This is just another form of OCD. We now call it 'scrupulosity' or having intrusive thoughts anathema to one's religious values. The more structured and rigid the religion, the more likely blasphemous thoughts can strike the OCD mind.

But there was no sin, only the thought. You've been fooled again."

I felt better, but I still couldn't stop the thoughts. I could only say, "So, the Jews and Catholics have a lot in common?"

"More than they'll ever admit," he said.

We had gotten even.

It began with the *bris*. The other people (the *goyim*) took our Adam, Eve, Moses, King David, the Passover, and then even took one of our boys to worship. They were so busy grabbing everything, they acquired our tendency toward OCD, too. So now, we've come a long way from my first ecumenical bris to the first ecumenical malady. Now we're even-steven.

I noticed an ad in the newspaper for the National OCD Foundation in Milford, Connecticut. I joined the St. Louis Chapter at St. John's Mercy Medical Center. I learned that the one thing the organizations didn't have was money. They had no spokesman like Michael J. Fox for Parkinson's Disease, but OCD sufferers walled in by horrendous obsessions have every bit as much pain as those with Parkinson's, spinal cord injuries, and even cancer. I realized that somehow my guardian angel was leading me toward fulfillment with my memoir and the possibility to become a spokesman for OCD groups. I had finally emerged from my wilderness and discovered my role in life. My egg had finally coalesced.

I attended one of the OCD support group meetings. I spied several brochures on a table, which shockingly described my pain and my feelings of being a *shlepper*. The condition was called

"Obsessive Slowness." Faced with conflicting thoughts, a person with OCD has a tendency to proceed cautiously and slowly. Thinking of two things at once causes confusion and difficulty making everyday decisions. Could this be why I always thought of myself as a *shlepper*?

I had come a long way, used every tool at my disposal, and finally succeeded in stopping my rituals. But something was missing. I had OCD without the rituals, but obsessive thoughts still plagued me. I had come out of my shell, but I still felt trapped. I had to take another step up my ladder.

I could hear Shleppriel calling me. "Spirituality is the key to inner contentment."*

"How?" I asked.

He said I would find my way. "Do *mitzvot,*" he said. If I reached out to people and honored my fellow man, I would not dwell on myself so much. The more I involved myself in attempting to help other people, the less time I'd have to be self occupied.

Could I relieve the obsessive tension clamped like a vise around my mind? By helping others, I would show my fellow OCDers there is hope. Working and helping others would keep me out of myself and out of my head, which has been my worst enemy.

WINGS OF EAGLES

 ～

"Circumcise the foreskin of your heart"
— Deuteronomy 10:16

For many years the mark of a Jew was the circumcision, but I've learned there's a spiritual circumcision that enabled me to overcome my self-centered obsessions. So did I understand the need for faith, and I remembered the "Bible Code." God had to open the foreskin of my heart as Moses said in Deuteronomy. Like a gravitational force, I felt drawn to Israel where the code predicted I would go as a *shlepper* to Jerusalem.

We made plans to fly on El Al, and took off for the promised land.

As we approached Tel Aviv, my wife and I, and many others, had tears in our eyes. We landed in Eretz Israel, the land of Abraham, Isaac, and Jacob, and now, according to my Bar Mitzvah Bible Code from 1945, Rudovey Fadem finally, fifty years later, had arrived, to fulfill its prediction.

We arrived on a Saturday at the Wall where Sabbath services were being held with the Torah portion having just been laid out on a table. A voice from the past called out to me to read from the scriptures. It was a smiling Meyer Schwab who greeted me.

Someone moved out of the shadows and approached me. He was tall and thin, wore a black suit and yarmulka. His face was hidden by a large bushy beard. He spoke in a high-toned voice.

"Are you still getting mustard and ketchup on your suits and ties?"

Oh my God! I looked at his beady eyes overlooking his beak of a nose.

"Dov? Is that you?"

"You were expecting Chanukah Harry?"

"A rabbi without a *bar mitzvah*?" I asked.

"No, a cantor who sings like a dove."

"What happened to the brokerage business?"

"I, unlike you, got tired of dealing *with* numbers. I found God's greatest blessing in the Book of Numbers."

He motioned me to read.

It had been fifty years since I had read Hebrew, but I read as I did at my bar mitzvah. Someone moved the scroll and my eyes lit up. The Bible Code had reappeared to me. The only difference was that the word "shlepper" had been crossed out. The word "mensch" took its place. I could hardly believe I was at the end of my journey and my odyssey of spiritual fulfillment.

*The Bible Code as it appeared in the
Torah at Rudovey Fadum's reading at
the Great Western Wall, June 15, 1999*

The sky was overcast, the sun wanting to break through, and Jews of every persuasion were praying.

With the crowd chanting and praying around me I drew closer to the Wall and kissed a stone. For a moment it was cold, but then it felt warm to me. A thought intruded. *Take the message out of the crack in the wall, take the message.*

How could I pick up a crumpled piece of parchment on which other people had written personal, heartfelt words? That would be an intrusion.

Pick up the message.

Pick it up.

Perhaps one message was for me.

I yielded. The parchment on which the message was scrawled looked ancient. I could not bring myself to read the words, so I slipped it into my pocket. Standing there before the Wall, I felt at peace. For the first time, my mind was clear, free from incessant thought.

But then, like a sudden thunderstorm, the old rituals, so long suppressed, started pounding, pounding like a hammer on my skull, demanding to burst forth. My tension swelled as I felt the necessity to knock my knuckles against the stones, stomp my feet a hundred times on the ground before the Wall. I buried my face in the Wall as I lay my hands on the cold stones and prepared to fight.

"No, no, don't happen here. Not here," I said.

Hate, hate, hate.

The hellish thoughts were back.

Hate God, hate God.

But the thought was not fact. *Not fact, not fact.* The demon is the devil tricking me into believing a lie; in fact, believing in him.

Hate God, hate God. No! Love God, love God.

I found truth in prayer. I invoked the Shma.

Shma Yisroel (Hear, O Israel).

Hate God, hate God.

A-doney Elohaeinu (O Lord our God).

Hate God.

A-donoy Ehad (The Lord is one).

Then I remembered the verse after the Shma, which says, "You will love the Lord your God with all your heart, with all your soul, and with all your might (Deut. 6:5).

I knew that God wanted me to love Him, but how could I? My heart felt cut to shreds by pangs of conscience. I wasn't sure I had a soul. As for all my might, I used that up controlling my errant thoughts, which left God pretty much out of the picture.

But here I was, saying the Shma, and I was thinking about God. The Shma said He was my God. He was there for me, but I had seldom been there for Him. My heart bled and my head throbbed. If only God would give me a sign!

Then, through the clouds a bright oval grew larger and larger until I could tell it was my old friend Shleppriel, floating as if on the wings of eagles.

"Hello, *Mensh*," he yelled.

"Who, me? What did I ever do to deserve that honor?"

"You've always been a *Mensh!* But you've believed in a lie. The demon tricked you into thinking you were a *Shlepper*. You thought that was the way God made you."

I protested, saying, "But I'm not a success! I'm not rich."

Shleppriel replied, "You've been reading the wrong book. Whoever said a *mensh* had to be rich? A real *mensh* is someone who laughs at his troubles and helps others to laugh along. The demon does not like laughter. He doesn't want people to be happy. Now, just look at you. You're pretty funny."

I looked askance and said, "You could have told me this a long time ago and saved me a lot of trouble."

He replied gently, "That would have made your book pretty boring."

He had a point. But I still felt like a *shlepper* and I still thought like a *shlepper* with OCD.

Shleppriel said, "Think positively. You have a lot of room for improvement. But you won't need me any more.

I protested. "Wait! You can't leave me like this! What about my vision? What about my ladder?"

Shleppriel laughed. "I'll tell you about ladders. I know about ladders. I was one of the angels in Jacob's dream. Ladders are for angels. When the time is right I'll take you up to the top. But now God has a special message for you."

"Oh!" I pulled the ancient scroll out of my pocket and carefully opened it. The message was from the Book of Numbers, chapter 6:24. I read the words of Aaron in ancient Hebrew:

May the Lord bless you and keep you.

May the Lord lift up His face upon you and be gracious unto you.

May the Lord lift up His face upon you and give you peace.

The words penetrated my aching heart. Could this be the answer to my wasted thoughts and tiresome rituals? Peace, yes, peace, peace! This is what I yearned for all my life. I could hardly constrain myself. God was penetrating my frozen compulsions. I looked over at my wife standing on the women's side of the wall and felt a strong sense of gratitude for her. Where would I be without her comfort and support? Beside her were the glowing faces of my two beautiful daughters, Kimmie and Michelle, my wife's priceless gifts to me.

I ran to share the message with them. When they saw me tripping toward them, they cried out, "Dad! What's wrong?"

I answered, "Wrong? Everything is right!"

I showed them the message. They embraced me with tears, overcome with joy that I was on the road to peace. "Shalom, shalom, shalom," I joyfully repeated. Blades of sunshine, like glistening knives, pierced the dark clouds and filled me with the warmth of *shalom*.

Epilogue

It has been four years since I stood before the Wall, and I have discovered something worth thinking about. That message was opening my mind to listen to God in the scriptures. I have thought about Cain, Abraham, and Aaron. I have thought deeply about the circumcision of my heart. Best of all, I have been thinking about God.

Sometimes I wonder if God has OCD, the way he loves to work with numbers. Think about it. He is the one who started the whole counting business. Open the Torah to the first page, and what do we get? He wasn't satisfied with one day. He took six, and then He rested. Or, one plague against Egypt was not enough — He counted to ten. When He got to the commandments, He again counted to ten.

God loves to count. According to the Book of Numbers, when Israel was in the wilderness, once was not enough. He had to count the Israelis twice! Sometimes things just don't add up, but for God, it is a simple matter of one, two, three. He numbers our days, so we can count on Him.

I admit that I have a long way to go on my way to peace. I still feel the inner conflict and self-doubt, yet it is different now. I know that God has blessed me with a sense of humor. That is one blessing I can share with people who have similar struggles. If I have made you smile just once, that would make me happy; twice, and I will be ecstatic.

My malicious obsession has finally become a magnificent obsession.

To all my fellow OCD sufferers:

I do not care whether you are Jewish, Catholic, Protestant, Muslim, black or white, we are all together. We share an anxiety disorder that may take a hundred different forms, but we all have a bond like brothers. If you should happen to have OCD, here's what you should do:

1. See a doctor or specialist and tell him or her every symptom bothering you.
2. If drugs are recommended, take them as a starting point.
3. Use every possible tool at your disposal. If possible, immediately start behavior therapy. For me, I also used humor, willpower, fantasy, music, and spirituality.
4. If you cannot stop the thoughts, let them float and train yourself not to react to them. The thought, no matter how terrifying, is not fact. It has nothing to do with reality.
5. The OCDemon has been deceiving you all through your life. He is a hoaxer whose goal is to torment you. The hell with him. He is a damnable bastard fiend who is out to make your life miserable. Strive to eliminate the Al-Qaeda of your mind.
6. You have a choice: give in, and like Howard Hughes, go down the drain, or fight. Be the victor, not the victim.
7. Try interrupting the chain of obsessive thoughts by focusing on something that calms you. For me, I let my beautiful music, especially Mozart, float through my mind. Whistling has always relaxed me.
8. I may have OCD, but OCD does not have me.
9. Get out of your head and help people. Relieve the pressures on your mind by helping others by doing *mitzvot* (good deeds).
10. If you happen to have OCD, don't give it a third thought.

THE NATIONAL OCD
FOUNDATION NEEDS YOU!

Howard Hughes had OCD, and it killed him. But hundreds of thousands of people can't afford treatment and they suffer with a pain equal to those with Parkinson's and cancer. If you can spare just one dollar, you can make a difference. However, if an intrusive thought should enter your mind, compelling you to say over and over again: *Give another dollar, give another dollar, give another dollar*, don't worry, you don't have OCD. Just go ahead and give to a good cause.

Send your dollars to:
Patricia Perkins-Doyle, J.D.
Executive director
Obsessive Compulsive Foundation
227 Notch Hill Road
North Branford, CT 06471
Tel: 203-315-2019
e-mail: info@ocfoundation.org
www.ocfoundation.org

ATTENTION ALL
ASPIRING ACTORS

ℒℴ

Log onto Shlepper-ocd.com, ocd.com, ocd.com, for roles in the film version of *The Memoirs of a Born Shlepper*. Send resume and picture.

To be honest, certain film stars have shown an interest: Kramer from "Seinfeld" to play Shleppriel. Jason Alexander to play me. Sharon Stone to play my wife.

Let it be known that if Sharon Stone, the quintessential blond *shikseh*, should agree, I will force myself to play myself. I must confess that I may need a stunt man to stand up for me. That role you can audition for.

Log On to the Newest
E-commerce Site

∽

www.shlepper-ocd.com SALE!

Last chance to get good, cheap *Bar Mitzvah* clothes from
1945.
Five ties: seventy-five cents each. Take your choice:
a) Blue tie with yellow mustard stain*
b) Red tie with glob of ketchup so red you'll hardly notice
c) Pink tie with salad dressing
d) Orange tie with soup
e) Green tie with butter.
Special: All five for only two dollars.
And, for the most discriminating taste, one original, finely wo-
ven, carefully petrified *Bar Mitzvah* suit with five stains: four
dollars and ninety-nine cents.
Plus, for the discriminating palate: one historical bagel and lox
sandwich left over in my right pocket: sixty-five cents.
Hurry, hurry, get 'em while they last!

---

* All stains are certified Kosher.

Testimonial

⟋⟍

April 29, 2003

" 'Trow 'em in the garbage."

Hard to believe that my first encounter with Rod Fadem, whom I have loved and admired for over seventy years, brought out the worst in me, and therefore that ugly exclamation!

I am proud to say, here and now, that the autobiography you have just consumed definitely brings out the best in him... however, if you disagree, merely " 'trow 'em in the garbage!"

Respectfully submitted,
Aaron J. Fadem (the older brother)

Quick Order Form

Fax orders: (419) 281-6883; please photocopy and send this form.

Phone orders: (800) 247-6653 (please have your credit card ready).

Email orders: info@bookmasters.com.

Postal orders: Bookmasters, Inc., P.O. Box 388, Ashland, OH 44805

Please send me _____ copies of *Memoirs of a Born Shlepper,* by Rod Fadem, at $15.95 each. I understand that I may return any of them for a full refund—for any reason, no questions asked.

Name: _____

Address: _____

City:_____ State:_____ Zip: _____

Telephone: _____

Email address: _____

Shipping:
  U.S.: $3.50 for the first book and
  $2.00 for each additional book.
  International: $9.00 for the first book and
  $5.00 for each additional book.

Payment: ❑ Check   ❑ Credit Card

  ❑ VISA   ❑ MasterCard   ❑ Optima

  ❑ AMEX   ❑ Discover

Card number: _____

Name on card: _____

Expiration date: _____ /_____